EVIDENCE AND INFERENCE

EVIDENCE
AND INFERENCE

The Hayden Colloquium on Scientific Concept and Method

EDITED BY

DANIEL LERNER

CONTRIBUTORS

Raymond Aron
Martin Deutsch
Erik H. Erikson
Jacob Fine

Henry M. Hart, Jr.
Paul F. Lazarsfeld
Daniel Lerner
John T. McNaughton

THE FREE PRESS OF GLENCOE

This group of essays originated in the Hayden Colloquium of the Massachusetts Institute of Technology and was first published in DAEDALUS, the Journal of the American Academy of Arts and Sciences.

—

CONTENTS

INTRODUCTION

On Evidence and Inference

DANIEL LERNER

THE STORY was told by Albert Einstein of the young man who had married a very plain wife. Asked whether he was happy, the young man replied: "To tell the truth, I have to lie."

This is Talmudism, an ancient variant of the general mode of logical disputation called dialectic. For the needs of debate, dialectic is a superb instrument. It cancels certainty by casting doubt; while feinting at the mind, it delivers a verbal blow to the solar plexus that leaves the opponent gasping and speechless. It scores, in short, "debater's points."

Why then does dialectic, once a major mode of intellectual discourse, now figure only at the level of persiflage and repartee? Why does this mode of drawing inference from evidence no longer seem appropriate for serious needs?

The answer lies largely in the reliance of dialectic on Sophic knowledge—in the ancient sense, knowledge "obtained by some secret process."[1] The dialectical inference derives from evidence which is "secret" because undisclosed, implicit. Such putative knowledge, since it is not shared by others, cannot be used by them.

On this point dialectic decisively parts company from science. The first test of scientific knowledge is that it must be public and not private, explicit and not "secret," available in a common fund for use by all who can learn. This test has a sociological derivation as well as a methodological consequence.

The sociology of scientific knowledge makes enlightening history. The requirement of a public, explicit, common fund of propositions was established only against heavy opposition through the centuries from the powerful personnel of the magic and religion industries. The struggle for a rational science of medicine against those skilled in charms, amulets, incantations, herbs, and leeches is well remembered. So is the struggle for an observational science of astronomy against those skilled in court astrology and clerical cosmology.[2]

The conception of knowledge as public disclosure to a common fund was, sociologically, the intellectual instrument by which a "new middle class" established itself between the dominant social orders and the ancient peasant mass. The growth of cities, the spread of literacy, the rise of universities, the reliance on inquiry—these were its institutional means. Through these institutions, the intellectual instrument was continuously extended to include all verifiable knowledge. Over the generations it captured from natural and social philosophy the several domains of inquiry now styled, with grand simplicity, Science.[3]

Faith in Science reached an apogee in the latter part of the nineteenth century in Victorian England, where the Newtonian universe was self-evident and the Spencerian gloss on Darwinian doctrine was persuasive. In twentieth-century Europe, following the collapse of the Pax Brittanica, the scientific creed came under sharp sociological challenge from a new "class," the professional political cadres of revolutionary counter-elites, discontented with their lot and ready to remake European society. The intellectual instrument of these new contenders was anti-Scientism, a manipulative mentality based on intuition rather than an investigative mentality based on evidence. Ludendorff, the spiritual presbyter of Nazism, bitterly attacked the scientistic Germany of his youth in these terms: "Wir lernten *sachlich statt persönlich* denken, wir waren Schwarmgeister statt Menschen der rauhen Wirklichkeit."[4] Hitler, following Ludendorff, delivered heavy blows to the scientific creed already sapped by Mussolini and Stalin.

Excited anti-Nazi philosophers in Europe forecast the "eclipse of reason." The historic achievement of human rationality seemed, early in the twentieth century, to be undermined by the totalitarian attack on objective science. Some humanists were confused by this sudden reversal of the secular trend of intellectual history which, over past centuries, had steadily extended free inquiry into new zones of human thought and feeling. They sought to salvage rationality by sacrificing science. Nervous intellectuals began to speak of Science and Wisdom as a dichotomy, seeking to disengage the latter from Nazi assaults upon the former. But these turned out to be philosophical categories which subsumed few empirical cases, analytic classes which included few observable members. To dichotomize Science and Wisdom was, it soon became clear, to provide fictions for fables.

The more conducive to a murderous Munich was this intellectual appeasement because it seemed to justify the totalitarian theory of knowledge. Ludendorff's insistence on the intuitive basis of action, on the superiority of introspective over objective knowledge, was no mere quibble over this or that scientific procedure. It was a root-and-branch onslaught against the whole modern conception of knowledge as a common fund of propositions explicitly formulated, empirically tested and objectively validated. The related sociology of knowledge as a public treasury available for use by anybody with adequate competence was, in the totalitarian view, merely an immoral evasion of authority by pusillanimous democracy. True knowledge, for the Nazis as for the Bolsheviks, was codified in the official ideology. New information could not be certified purely by valid inference from verifiable evidence but had first to be declared compatible with doctrines sanctified by the totalitarian power. On this test of truth humanists were at least as likely as scientists to founder—more likely, indeed, since the propositions that matter to humanists are frequently at the core of the totalitarian code. As humanists soon discovered, the totalitarians rejected the whole modern conception of knowledge as the outcome of public procedures disciplined, in Lecky's phrase, by "the due exercise of private judgment."[5]

The larger meaning of the totalitarian offensive against modern knowledge was investigated more usefully by other than nervous literati. Social scientists studied the altered social setting of twentieth century Europe to determine those features of contemporary life which lent plausibility to the outlandish and reactionary dogmas of the totalitarians. The late Danish sociologist, Svend Ranulf, scrutinized the social background of Nazi epistemology in his remarkable study *Hitler's Battle Against Objectivity*.[6] The psychoanalyst Erik H. Erikson clarified the profound impact of this Nazi attack upon objectivity in a brilliant analysis of "Hitler's Imagery and German Youth."[7]

Of direct relevance to the volume in hand were the emerging "schools" of young thinkers vigorously re-examining the logical foundations of the scientific creed throughout interbellum Europe —in Vienna, in Warsaw, in Cambridge (England). Their studies reinvigorated contemporary thinking in mathematics, the physical sciences and, more recently, the social sciences.[8] With the push of Bolshevism, Fascism, and Nazism through Europe, many of these European thinkers migrated to America. Rigorous reconsideration in this country of the assumptions underlying science, and the social order in which it had flourished, was stimulated by their coming.

The process is reflected in the cosmopolitan composition of this Colloquium on "Evidence and Inference." Only in preparing for publication was it realized that four of the five articles were written by persons reared in Europe. Two are Viennese who received their higher education in Paris and Cambridge (at M.I.T.); one was born in Germany of Danish parentage and was trained in Vienna; one is French, with post-doctoral training in Germany. The rich continental heritage of the different fields represented in this Colloquium is indicated by this unexpected European confluence on a set of core problems in scientific concept and method.

While these contributions reveal the diversity of researches in progress in the several fields of academic work, they are unified by attention in each case to the classic concern of evidence and inference. Ancient philosophy attacked these problems through dialectical analysis of the nature of knowledge (epistemology) and of the material known (ontology), with logic codifying the formal rules of rational discourse. Modern European thinking reshaped these concerns over the past century in the image of a probabilistic universe, in which verifiable knowledge tends to be experimental, quantitative, and subject to a factor of "human error" that must enter into the calculus. This bespeaks, despite our devoted tracing of intellectual lineage from the ancient Athenians, a new environment for the modern theory of knowledge. The newness is exemplified in two modes of empirical inquiry—statistical and psychological—which did not exist in Talmudic Israel or Socratic Athens.

Consider the disciplines represented in this Colloquium. We begin with history and law (Aron and Hart-McNaughton), matters in which the ancients were highly sophisticated; we conclude with nuclear physics (Deutsch), which was unknown to them. In the middle are psychoanalysis and social psychology, which deal with matters familiar to the Greeks but by unheard-of concepts and methods. Between Sophocles' dramatic Oedipus theme and Erikson's clinical Oedipus complex, between Socrates' commentary on Athenian opinion and Lazarsfeld's methodology of attitude research, there intervene many transformations of intellectual climate, of which the most decisive is the scientific transformation in the past few centuries. As Kirtley Mather has put it: "To understand aright the revolution which has been accomplished in the minds of thoughtful men during the last few generations, one must comprehend the fact that the world of the pre-scientific age was utterly different from our world."[9]

The intellectual transformation "accomplished in the minds of thoughtful men" shows, for example, in contemporary attitudes toward the study of man. Only "during the last few generations" have we moved from metaphysical speculation on Human Nature to empirical investigation of human behavior—from theologies of Man as image of God (or vice versa) to psychologies of what man is in terms of what he does. To grasp how profoundly new is this view of man, which underlies what we nowadays call Social Science, recall that medical theorists of the eighteenth century remained preoccupied (even after Harvey's demonstration of blood circulation) with the Hippocratic question "whether in disease there is not something supernatural"—despite Hippocrates' own rejection of magic in his famous writing *On The Sacred Disease.*

The difficulties of disengaging behavioral descriptions from supernatural dicta in medicine, which dealt only with the human body, have been multiplied for Social Science owing to its protean concern with every variety of human behavior—sexuality and piety, work and wealth, leisure and health. Under the rule of Social Science there are no eternal mysteries in human behavior, but only phenomena that have not yet been adequately observed. Nothing human is inscrutable; all behavior is amenable to inquiry. But as the medical arts found it difficult to disengage from magic, so the social sciences are still surrounded by the ancient sense of mystery. In the year 1959, a group of eminent American social scientists published a full-scale symposium in response to this problem posed by the editor of a leading French humanistic review: "The basic question is this: what, approximately, is the possible boundary between the known and the unknown, the analyzable and the mysterious, in the theory and practice of the scientific study of man?"[10]

What differentiates the responses of the American social scientists to this ancient question from, say, the *Protagoras* of Plato or the *Guide* of Maimonides is the set of concepts and methods associated with modern psychology and statistics to which the classical dialecticians had no access. The fundamental concept of modern psychology, as suggested above, is the postulate that human nature can be inferred from human behavior. An immediate consequence of this postulate, rigorously applied, is to divorce observation from valuation—to disengage behavioral evidence from moral inferences of right and wrong, good and bad. Instead, the principal categories of social science for classifying human behavior are "normal" and "deviant."

The psychological concept of normalcy arose from, and in turn reinforced, the more generous and humane conceptions of aberrant behavior evolved by the modern mind. Normal behavior was no longer regarded as divinely prescribed, hence deviations from normalcy did not have to be diabolically instigated. Mental disease moved from the occult province of demonology into the enriched field of medical science. As a result, the "village idiot" was liberated from his ancient role as an accursed and unclean imp, the fated butt of human brutality; instead he was assigned the human and dignified status of a mental patient suffering from personality disorder. This new conception of "normalcy," which humanized the lives of many millions of deviant and aberrant persons around the world over the past century, was the outcome of modern scientific thinking applied to antique conceptions of human nature.

In this process the probabilistic universe of scientific method played a key role. Sir Charles Sherrington, reviewing the evolution of man's conceptions of himself, has shown the persistent anxiety among thoughtful men that Science should not reveal the world to be "a purely material product by Chance out of Chaos." That anxiety was not fully allayed until the development of statistics, over the past century, provided scientists with tools for observing and ordering the probabilistic universe—for clarifying the rationale that underlies events produced "by Chance out of Chaos." Nowadays, we deal efficiently with this universe, formerly so frightening even to trained minds, by randomizing Chaos and probabilizing Chance.[11] Once an effective method for dealing with a universe codified by statistical rules was available, the idea of such a universe lost its terror. As Sherrington puts it: "The materialism of antiquity sat and looked at Nature, impotent to deal with her. It made her a thing to stare at and despair. The reasoned materialism of today is on the contrary an inspiration for dealing with Nature."[12]

The statistical method wedded to the psychological concept produced our modern perspective of "normalcy" in human behavior —of the normal not as the correct behavior prescribed in some sacred code, but as *a range* of behaviors observed around the mean (or median or mode) of a frequency distribution of empirical conduct. If there are no longer any eternal mysteries, in the probabilistic universe, neither are there any more eternal verities. The truth is the closest statistical approximation to the observed occurrence of events. This conception brought man into the realm of nature; the great achievements of natural science acquired in this way made possible a modern social science. Some problems varied greatly as between natural and social science, while others retained common and constant features. It was in codifying the rules of reliable evidence and valid inference that ancient and modern thinking, dialectical and scientific minds, tended most sharply to diverge.

A distinctive accomplishment of the past generation has been to make this divergence explicit, to investigate its sources and to seek ways of closing the scientific gap between the natural and social sciences. The present Colloquium represents extremely well the fruits of this effort in the contemporary intellectual scene. Let us take the hallmark of scientific thinking to be the quest for regularities underlying diverse events, the recurrent normal distributions produced by various sets of observations—in short, the invariants accounting for variable behavior (not "laws," be it understood, but high-probability forecasts of future relationships).

By this criterion, our Colloquium divides into two groups. The first three papers deal, in a modern framework, with problems well understood in the pre-scientific age, problems of the particular case and the personal judgment. The investigator's task is to assemble the relevant evidence and then to judge whether the array means A or B: true or false, innocent or guilty, well or ill. The historian, the judge, the physician follow methodological procedures that hinge upon a common characteristic: their personal judgment must play the decisive role in assembling the evidence, drawing the inference, and formulating the conclusion in each case they consider. The judge is, and must be, involved in the events whose meaning he judges.

This is the nature of the clinical situation. As Erikson says: "The clinician, . . . appointed to judge the bit of interrupted

life put before him . . . finds himself part of another man's most
intimate life history." Aron, in turn, tells us that the historian
"seeks to recognize himself among his ancestors or, conversely, to
take account of what he is by discovering what others have been."
Hart and McNaughton, in unraveling the skein of "adjudicative"
and "legislative" facts from which legal decisions are woven, show
us why introspection is organic to clinical inquiry. The clinician
must decide single "cases" rather than, like the scientist, establish
regularities among diverse events (with only limited liability for
the "case" in which any event occurs).

The authors of these three papers are keenly aware of this common bond between their disciplines. Aron likens the historian's
role to that of the *juge d'instruction,* the man whose personal
judgment is decisive in a court of inquiry. Hart and McNaughton,
dealing with adjudicative facts as historical facts, point out the
many technical traditions designed to safeguard the personal and
introspective component of the judicial decision. Thus, the long
tradition of "excluded evidence" (hearsay, opinion) reflects "the
fear that the evidence will be given *too much weight.*" And "expert testimony" may be disregarded solely because of the judge's
"lack of a sense of competence in dealing with it."

These papers clarify the acute methodological problem of the
"probability of a single case."[13] How can the scientific method
evolved to investigate a probabilistic universe of recurrent events
be adapted to the adjudication of historical "cases," singular and
non-recurrent? Aron formulates the historian's problem sharply and
suggests that, given the nature of his material, probability methods
can have only limited utility for historical logic. Hart and Mc-
Naughton point out that, neither certainty nor consistency being
required by the court, even "the probabilities are determined in
a most subjective and unscientific way." Especially interesting is
their observation on judicial exclusion of statistical evidence, "The
court somehow feels more comfortable permitting a finding to be
based on eye-witness testimony even though the probative value
of such testimony is itself determined ultimately by home-spun
'statistics' in the mind of the triers of fact and . . . is probably
no more indicative of the truth than the [statistical] evidence."

Erikson sees the clinical situation in somewhat closer relation
to the probabilistic universe of scientific method. The psychoanalyst
is not confined, like the historian and the judge, to past events.

While his aim is to diagnose a life-history, he can base his reconstruction of the past upon a continuous series of observations in the present. These permit ". . . the gradual establishment of strategic intersections on a number of tangents that eventually makes it possible to locate in the observed phenomena that central core which comprises the 'evidence.' " Moreover, the psychoanalyst, again unlike the historian and the judge, works with a comprehensive, and more or less unified, theory. This codifies clinical procedures (the making, classifying, and interpreting of observations) sufficiently, in Erikson's judgment, to conclude that ". . . there is enough method in our work systematically to force favorite assumptions to become probable inferences. . . ."

The first group of papers thus carries us through the common problems and divergent procedures of the clinical mode of inquiry. The core methodological concern, for historian, jurist, and physician, is how to use the partial regularities disclosed by scientific investigation to fortify, without overpowering, the introspective element needed to make net judgments on particular cases.

The second group of papers reverses this epistemological emphasis with quite important consequences for concept and method. What Lazarsfeld and Deutsch share is a common confidence in the probabilistic universe of science and a common concern that our introspective or intuitive insights should be *worthy* of the powerful apparatus of scientific inquiry.

Thus, as Erikson leads us out of the dialectical universe of discourse via the acknowledgment of probability, so Lazarsfeld leads us into the scientific universe via the problem of aggregation. How to match available units of observation with desired units of interpretation is the problem set by Lazarsfeld. Or, in terms of the problems posed by Hart and McNaughton, what regularities of guilt can be determined that will enable a judge to decide better (with lower chances of error) whether a particular defendant in a particular "case" is guilty or not? What regularities of power can be established, to take Aron's problem, that will enable an historian to decide whether a particular nation is strengthening or weakening?

Martin Deutsch moves us from the problematics of research on human behavior to the simple elegance of nuclear physics—often considered the apex of scientific inquiry today—where research on the physical universe is compromised only by the human behavior of the experimenter. But to this bit of behavior, Deutsch attributes a very large role, "The decisive intuition of the experimenter is really the ability to *recognize relevance* in the evidence presented by the experiment."

Intuition, in this usage, differs significantly from the decisive introspection of the historian-jurist-clinician. First, the physicist's intuition may determine the originality of his experiments, but it does not literally "decide" their outcome. The validity and reliability of experimental results are decided by objective canons which are quite independent of the experimenter's intuition. Intuition, in this sense, counts more for the experimenter than for the experiment.

Moreover, the physicist's intuition operates mainly on data which he himself creates. Whether Napoleon lost his reserves of power in Russia, whether John Doe robbed Richard Roe, whether the patient under observation hated his father—these are questions concerning past events that occurred once and for all, and no data can be "created" that will rearrange their timing, sequence or context. Whether velocity increases with pressure given constant temperature, whether the rate of learning decreases with age for persons of either sex—these are questions concerning a regularity in recurrent events, and data *can* be created to test these relationships in any time or place.

The quest for regularities and the capacity to create its own data differentiate scientific from historico-clinical methodology. They underlie the tendency in scientific work toward abstraction and generalization. Hence, while jurists feel most comfortable with "eye-witness testimony," physicists are less deferential to sheer observation—as Deutsch puts it, to "methods which give the illusion of direct sensory perception of the events involved." Nor does Lazarsfeld find such methods especially helpful on problems of aggregration.

The lessened scientific reliance on sensory observation does not, however, reflect any "dehumanization of science." On the contrary, and in ways that are not at all paradoxical, the second group of papers reveals a great reliance on the percipient person. But they require from him more than sharp sight or keen hearing. The valuable observer, for scientific purposes, works with a large intellectual context for his perceptions. His intuition is a high-gain, wide-range radar, alert to all significant cues in his environment.

Lazarsfeld speaks of this quality as "the image" with which the scientific worker goes about his analytic chores. Deutsch speaks of the "anthropomorphic image" which guides the experimenter's choice of research design. These variant expressions give the percipient person his large and indispensable place in even the most rigorous procedures of modern science. Introspection enjoys a major assignment, but it is instrumental and not merely self-indulgent. Introspection helps to close the gap between the body of evidence assembled and the inference drawn from this evidence. Closing this gap is the meaning of rigor. Introspection is then rewarded, in appropriate scientific manner, by being called into question and subjected to test.

✻ ✻ ✻

These papers originally were delivered as lectures in the first Hayden Colloquium of the Massachusetts Institute of Technology. Sponsored by the M.I.T. School of Humanities and Social Studies, from funds granted by the Carnegie Corporation of New York, the Hayden Colloquium explores the common intellectual concerns of the arts and sciences. The present set of papers reconsiders the classic problems of evidence and inference in the light of contemporary research. Our thanks are due to Dr. Jacob Fine, whose excellent case study, an appropriate supplement to the Hayden Colloquium, is reprinted here from the special issue of *Daedalus* (Fall 1958) in which the Colloquium was first published. We owe thanks as well to Dr. Gerald Holton, general editor of the American Academy of Arts and Sciences, for valuable aid from start to end; to Miss Christine Gainer, who labored mightily in this vineyard before the fruit became visible; to my wife, Jean Lerner, who as always scored the final runs. Future sessions of the Hayden Colloquium will set in a contemporary framework other classic problems of scientific concept and method; the topic scheduled for 1959 is "Quantity and Quality."

NOTES

1. William Little, H. W. Fowler, and J. Coulson, *The Oxford Dictionary on Historical Principles*, rev. and ed. C. T. Onions (3rd rev. ed.; Oxford: Clarendon Press, 1955), p. 1946.

2. These struggles are detailed in the great histories of science by Lynn Thorndike, Charles H. Haskins, George Sarton. A lively popular account of the

sixteenth century transition is H. M. Pachter, *Magic Into Science: The Story of Paracelsus* (New York: Schuman, 1951).

3. See Daniel Lerner (ed.), *The Human Meaning of The Social Sciences* (New York: Meridian Books, 1959), Part I.

4. Erich Ludendorff, Introduction to *Kriegsführung und Politik* (Berlin, 1923).

5. W. E. H. Lecky, *Rationalism in Europe* (New York: Appleton, 1888), II, 76.

6. Svend Ranulf, *Hitlers Kampf gegen der Objektivität* (Copenhagen: Ejnar Munksgaard, 1940).

7. Erik H. Erikson, "Hitler's Imagery and German Youth," *Psychiatry*, V (1942), 475-493.

8. See the philosophic efforts represented by Arne Naess in *An Empirical Study of The Expressions 'True,' 'Perfectly Certain' and 'Extremely Probable'* and *Interpretation and Preciseness* (Oslo: Jacob Dybwad, 1953). See also the reading list for the Lazarsfeld paper in this volume.

9. Kirtley Mather, *Science in Search of God* (New York: Holt, 1928), p. 4.

10. See "La Signification Humaine des Sciences Sociales aux Etats-Unis," special issue of *Esprit*, No. 269 (January 1959). The expanded American edition of this symposium is cited above in note 3.

11. I. Todhunter, *A History of The Mathematical Theory of Probability* (New York: Chelsea, 1949).

12. Sir Charles Sherrington, *Man On His Nature* (New York: Anchor Books, 1955), pp. 26, 265-266.

13. See Hans Reichenbach's essay on this topic in D. Lerner and H. D. Lasswell, eds., *The Policy Sciences* (Stanford, Calif.: Stanford University Press, 1952).

Evidence and Inference in History

RAYMOND ARON

I CONFESS that I feel apprehensive about the subject proposed to me. Even though there may be possible French equivalents to *evidence* and *inference*, the two concepts which guide this Colloquium, they are not part of my spontaneous vocabulary. The concept *evidence* refers, I believe, to an accumulation of data available to the scholar, in this case the historian, before he risks making *inferences*, i.e., operations leading to more or less general propositions which were not included in the facts but nevertheless may be legitimately deduced, inferred, or extracted from them. These two concepts embrace a vast territory. The first includes the documents of the historian as well as the experimental results of the physicist or the statistics of the sociologist. The second includes the hypotheses of an Einstein as well as the psychological hypotheses of the Soviet expert who, given the data concerning the great purge, imagines the motivations of Stalin or the impersonal mechanism by which the purge triumphed.

It would be surprising if such vast concepts posed a simple and one-dimensional problem. On the contrary, these concepts embrace *all* the problems of the experimental sciences, both those that classical logic subsumes under the categories of induction and deduction, and those suggested by analytical psychology and by comprehensive sociology. Furthermore, the distinction which we have established between data and inferences has a deceptive clarity. No one denies that in the most advanced natural sciences yesterday's inferences are today's givens. Propositions established mainly by means of inference become the data of which the scientist speaks. Theories and facts are integrated in such a manner that one would attempt in vain to separate them rigorously. Occa-

---

* Translated by Dr. Suzanne Keller and Mrs. Judith K. Davison.

sionally new facts force a reconsideration of theories, but even these new facts are data only with respect to the theories thereby put into question.

Psychologically, I agree that one must discriminate at any moment between the data gathered by the scientist and the inferences made from them. Logically, however, in the development of a science the same propositions have taken turns as inferences and data. Are we to engage in a study of the psychology of the scientist or of the logic of scientific procedure?

The uncertainty is even greater in the case of history—should we say scientific history? The object of history (not to be confused with the social sciences) is reality, which by its nature no longer is and will never again be. The decline of the Roman Empire occurred once and once only. It was unique (*einmalig*, as the Germans say) and nothing can be done to make it occur a second time. Thus, historical comprehension, as it has been interpreted throughout the centuries, necessarily requires the taking hold of that which "one will never see twice" as the poet would have it. (I employ the vague term to "take hold of" precisely because any more exact term such as "understand," "explain," "relate," would be debatable.)

Thus we arrive at one meaning of the antithesis *evidence-inference*. By definition, we have direct experience only of the present and never of the past, which as such has plunged into non-being. The data are the artifacts, the texts and the temples, the medals and the inscriptions, the ruins and the tombs, in brief, all that is included in the English terms of *records* and *remains*, all that we call in French *documents* and *monuments, témoignages* and *œuvres*—for *œuvres*, too, bear witness to the ideas and sentiments which gave rise to them.

I hesitate, however, to adopt this meaning of the antithesis proposed to me for discussion. To discuss it, one would have invited a professional historian, not a philosopher. For only the professional really knows what is required to reconstruct the past from documents left to us by the blind selection of time. Again, do I err in using the singular? The difficulties of such reconstruction are quite different for the specialist who seeks to decipher Cretan inscriptions and for the specialist who seeks, in the manner of a prosecuting attorney, to reconstruct the circumstances in which Hitler gave the order to exterminate six million Jews. In other words, the establishment of past facts from contemporary documents, logically the first step for the historian, poses, according to the epoch and order of the facts, quite different problems, which can be reduced to a single dimension only by an arbitrary simplification.

A second way of looking at these concepts brings us to what is generally called historical synthesis, or, more vaguely still, historical interpretation. In this case, the data would no longer be the available documents or monuments, but past facts hypothetically reconstituted as the initial step of the historical analysis. This second view is also not without its difficulties, however. If it is true that ultimately the pure fact (Caesar was assassinated on the Ides of March) is easily distinguishable from the interpretation (the republican government of Rome was doomed in any case) or from the hypothesis (Caesar intended to build an Oriental type of monarchy), there are all the intervening elements: the brute fact of the assassination is of no interest to anyone if it is not to put into the situation *(ensemble)* constituted by the crisis in the Roman republic, the opposition of the Senatorial aristocracy to personal power, etc. All these intervening elements, however, are neither brute facts nor interpretations; they are facts rendered intelligible by the ideas employed, by the progressive re-creation of the historico-social situation. It is in relation to this situation that new data derive their meaning, as experiments in physics or in chemistry contain a new lesson in relation to established laws or theories.

The notion of interpretation with respect to facts no more provides the theme we seek than the notion of past facts with respect to available documents. Facts and interpretations are too intertwined, and interpretations are too diversified in type, to permit global treatment of historical interpretation. But having set aside the two classical distinctions of documents—facts and facts-interpretations— i.e., both historical criticism and historical synthesis—what route remains open for us? Let us ask what the subject matter of historical inquiry is. Or, what is the historian's own intention, what is the specific aim (*l'intentionalité*) of historical science? To reply that the historian wants to know what has happened is to make the historian into a chronicler. But history is not a chronicle. Historical knowledge is not a simple accumulation of facts. Elaborated by the living, it tends to reconstitute the existence of the dead. It is determined simultaneously by the curiosity of the living and by the scientific intention not to imagine what might have been, but to establish what was. It differs from the natural sciences* and even from the social sciences, which seek to explain what was, is, or will be. It has in common with these disciplines the desire for rigor, proof, and approximation of reality.

The following bear particularly on the steps which lead to what is commonly called historical synthesis (although several concern the passage from documents to facts). But they will be organized with reference to the aims of the historian. If we agree that he seeks to assert nothing that is not in accord with the data, toward what do his inferences aim? That one seeks to explain phenomena in order to predict them, and thus eventually to control them, is self-evident. To say that one wishes to know what occurred at a given place and date is not immediately intelligible. The event will not be reproduced, the Roman empire will not be reborn. What does one want to know about what is past? Is the subject of historical science contained in the facts or is it simply compatible with them?

I

Since history is not a chronicle, it seeks to do something more than merely list facts or align events through time. It seems to me that this something more is composed of four elements. First, historical facts are also human facts, social facts. Men, similar to and different from us, have lived under the institutions which we are analyzing, they have adhered to beliefs of which their temples and their statues bear witness. The historian goes to meet other men, other peoples. He seeks to recognize himself among his ancestors or, conversely, to take account of what he is by discovering what others have been.

Secondly, events do not follow each other in the regular manner of the seasons or in the seemingly incoherent manner of rain and fine weather. The historian is curious to find out how things happened, why the Roman empire disintegrated—whether the internal crisis of the empire made inevitable the fatal outcome, or whether the empire, still vigorous, was accidentally struck a blow by the Barbarian invasions.

Thirdly, the historian does not collect the facts, but reconstitutes them into *ensembles*. Each of the historical disciplines assumes the legitimacy of certain divisions, of the reality (though partial and limited) of historical units such as empire, epoch, or civilization.

---

* Except those branches of the physical or the biological sciences which seek to reconstruct the history of the earth and of natural phenomena.

In the fourth place, the historian is tempted when he faces a certain *ensemble*, not only to fix its beginning and end, but also to reconstitute the intermediary stages, to compare the modality of change in one historical unit with that in another.

In sum, four questions seem to me to characterize the basic aims of the historian. How did the human actors live? Why and how did it happen? What are the historical configurations? What are the patterns of change? That is, we want to *understand the human actors, explain the events, elaborate historical units consistent with the articulation of reality, and discover whether there are great lines of evolution which either humanity as a whole or each historical unit follows.*

Several problems are raised by this list. What, precisely, does each question signify? Is the distinction among these four questions purely methodological and abstract, or does it have a philosophical import? Is the list complete? Let us take a simple example, where the abundance of documentation obviates difficulties arising from inadequacy of data, namely, the war of 1914.

The historian who is studying its origins cannot avoid trying to understand the actors. What did Bethmann-Hollweg, Wilhelm II, the Austro-Hungarian ministers, the Czar and his ministers think, seek, or know? An account of what occurred would be stripped of its dramatic and human dimensions if we confined ourselves only to the events, if we observed only the actions without understanding what took place in the minds of these historical personages. In a sense, a purely objective account, in the style adopted by certain American and French writers (for example, by Albert Camus in *L'Etranger*), would not only be unintelligible but absurd: events, diplomatic notes, and conversations between ministers and ambassadors are facts of experiences lived through by thinking beings, of meanings sought by them. An account of events, by definition, involves an understanding of the actors.

It also involves, more or less explicitly, an effort to answer the second question. The question *why* and *how* "it happened" take on multiple meanings, depending on our level of discourse. The *why* may sometimes be concerned with the intentions of one or more actors (what did the Austro-Hungarian ministers seek by their ultimatum to Serbia?), sometimes with so-called long-term and underlying forces rather than with the immediate causes which led to war. Yet, the historical account of the war of 1914 does not involve the third and fourth questions. Not that it does not include certain historical units (after all, when we speak of the war of 1914 we create an historical unit), but the historian of the twentieth century is not obliged to situate the war of 1914 in the historical unit which Spengler and Toynbee have christened "Western Civilization." Nor is he obliged, in the manner of Toynbee, to look for an analogy between the Peloponnesian War and the war of 1914, or between twentieth-century wars and those of the declining Roman Empire. (We reserve the question whether historians, in spite of themselves, do not in fact raise such questions.)

Though the first two questions are inseparable at the microscopic level, and though the last two questions are dismissed by the positivistic historian, all four questions can be interpreted to translate an ultimate question which man asks about his past. The first, ultimately, goes back to the mystery of human identity and human diversity; the second, to the mystery of the event, i.e., the intersection between necessity and accident; the third seeks the origin and consistency of the *ensemble* (period, civilization); the last is concerned with change in the double sense of direction and of meaning.

In this way, we see why some books of historical science are inspired by the first question, others by the second. Historians like Burckhardt, who seek to reconstruct and comprehend an epoch, are less anxious to follow the dramatic turns of wars and revolutions. But the historian who ponders the decline of Rome or the Napoleonic epic, desires above all to unravel the skein of cause and effect, to assess the responsibility of the masses and the great men, of blind necessity and human error, of that which had to be and that which no human will could have prevented.

In contrast, the last two questions do not suggest two approaches to historical science. At one extreme they mark the fundamental uncertainties in historical reconstruction, at the other they open up the supreme uncertainties regarding the human past or perhaps mankind as a whole (is it unitary or multi-dimensional? whither mankind?). That both the philosophy and the science of history are concerned with the same question should come as no surprise, for the meaning of any question is changed by the level on which it is raised. Suppose we are concerned with a battle, a favorite example of historical logicians as well as novelists: in what sense is a battle a unit? Is this unit real or is it created by the observer? Whatever the answer, the historian has no difficulties or doubts about using the elementary units as though they were real in his account. When Marx writes that human history consists of certain epochs—primitive communism, Asiatic mode of production, and economy founded upon slavery (antiquity), serfdom (Middle Ages), and wages (capitalism)—is he discovering the facts of history as they are inscribed in reality or is he creating these immense *ensembles* by the very concepts he utilizes? The same question arises, even more insistently, about the cultures and societies in the sense of the terms as used by Spengler and Toynbee.

The relationship among these four questions will emerge more clearly at the end of our analysis. Even if the distinction among them is not entirely arbitrary, as I believe, it suffices to accept it as a methodological one. This permits us to delineate four problems in historical inference: understanding the actors; historical determinism; a grasp of the *ensemble;* and the pattern of change. Everyone will agree that we are dealing with authentic problems, if not all problems.

II

Perhaps the best way to approach the theme of historical understanding is to choose an example. To select one where our understanding is not hampered by lack of data, let us take the leaders of the Soviet Union. Since they are contemporaries, we can see them, talk with them, and add their words, their gestures, and their faces to their books. But this makes no fundamental difference in the problem of historical understanding—as between members of the Politburo and, say, Roman Senators in the time of Caesar. Historians who have not known Lenin and his comrades will try to understand them, *mutatis mutandis*, just as they try to understand Pericles, who "waged the Peloponnesian War," or Caesar, who "crossed the Rubicon."

At the simplest level, understanding Pericles, Caesar, or Lenin, and their epoch-making decisions, is facilitated by what we shall call de-personalization. The more the actor is reduced to a role, the more he is defined by the objectives of his action, and the more Pericles is confused with the Athenian Commander-in-Chief, Caesar with the Pretender to the Monarchy, Lenin with the Revolutionary impatient to seize power, the less uncertain will our understanding be. The fact is that Pericles dominated Athenian politics when the Peloponnesian

War broke out, that Caesar crossed the Rubicon, and that Lenin gave the order for the coup d'état which initiated the seven days that shook the world. The more the historian sticks to events, the more he reduces men to their historical personage, the less he is tempted to fathom the hearts and minds of men.

But the historian who confined himself to stating that the Bolshevik leaders successfully engineered a coup d'état in the autumn of 1917, who explained their conduct by the favorable circumstances created by the war and revolution, would be singularly superficial. Lenin and his comrades adhered to a political doctrine which put their own undertaking into doubt. According to this doctrine, socialism should succeed capitalism when the productive forces had reached a stage of development not yet reached in Russia. The historian of the Russian Revolution and Soviet regime must therefore render intelligible the manner in which Lenin and his followers adjusted their conduct to their doctrine, the interpretations they gave to each event, the circumstances, their temperaments, etc.

If we wish to grasp more directly the aim, and the problem, of this kind of understanding, let us turn from Lenin to Khrushchev. When the latter announces that in a thermo-nuclear war capitalism will be destroyed while socialism will triumph, is he sincere or not? How does he envisage the inevitable triumph of socialism? What are the distinctive traits of the socialism whose triumph is inevitable? What historical vision governs the actions of the current Party Secretary? What are his rules of tactics and strategy? These questions are not academic but political since the answers to them imply predictions about the future decisions of the Communist leaders. In this sense, according to a banal formula, historical reconstruction is *retrospective foresight*. It seeks to elaborate the system of interpretation which would have made possible a prediction of the actual course of events.

If we keep to our example of the Communist leaders, certain observations suggest themselves immediately. Historical understanding, one often hears, demands that the historian be detached from himself and that he recognize the differences between himself and his fellow men. Nothing is more correct than this banality. The source of many errors committed by President Roosevelt was his conviction that he was dealing with men like himself, democrats somewhat given to violence but, in the last analysis, accessible to reason and to the reasoning of an American politician. The whole idea of the Big Three (or Big Two) which would establish and maintain peace after the defeat of Germany and Japan rested on the belief that the Communist leaders are "men like us," whose vision of the world did not differ essentially from that of the American leaders, who did not see the interests of Russia or Communism as fundamentally opposed to American or European interests. Men of history —of whom the historian is the interpreter—change.

But these changing men also bear certain resemblances to each other, without which the historian would be incapable of understanding them. Historical understanding consists of perceiving differences among similar phenomena and similarities among different ones. In the example we have chosen, the differences arise on the level of world perspective, of the hierarchy of values, of tactical rules for action, of ultimate objectives, of hypotheses about the course of history—in short, of ways of conceiving the historico-political world. Let us translate the lesson of this example into abstract terms: the man who changes with respect to societies and time is cultural man. These changes are not incompatible with the stability of biological man, of logical functions or psychological mechanisms. Soviet man does not have a socialistic physics; he rejects psychoanalysis, but psychoanalysts do not have to adopt other theories to understand him. Psychoanalysis explains different men by applying the same concepts.*

When the aim is to understand the actors, what, then, is the relation between data and inferences? The data are various written records, words, monuments. The objective of historical science is not to know everything (we will never finish collecting all the records of the Bolsheviks), but to understand the *ensemble*. It is impossible to establish a rigorous distinction between data and inferences, between what we know as fact and what we infer from the facts. The past conduct of the Communist leaders constitutes the evidence on which we base our inferences about their future conduct. Given the manner of reasoning of Stalin and his associates, should we have expected the sovietization of the "liberated" countries after the occupation of Eastern Europe by the Russian army? On what does the answer given by the "experts" rest? On long familiarity with the documents, on deep analysis of the ideology of the Communist system,

---

* Is it necessary to point out that this analysis of similarity and difference in understanding men is greatly simplified? Anthropologists and ethnologists also face this problem. The level of formalization at which the constancy of human nature is found cannot be determined *a priori* and theoretically.

and on hypotheses about the psychology of Stalin himself. An hypothesis is *confirmed* by the events it enables us to predict. It would be dangerous to say it has been verified, because an hypothesis—a certain system of thought or a certain psychological mechanism—is not the only one on the basis of which inferences can be made. (Would a Czarist government have tried to make permanent its domination of Eastern Europe or not? Is it the ideology of the universal spread of Communism which accounts for the sovietization of Eastern Europe or the simple concern for the "national interest" of the Russian State?)

The relationship between facts and inferences, in the effort to understand the actors, is legitimately circular. What does a given statement by an actor mean? To minimize the chances of erroneous interpretation, we must know the pattern of his thought. But how can we get at such a pattern of thought if not by accumulation of details? The interchange between the part and the whole is inevitable and legitimate. Proof emerges little by little, by elaboration of the parts and grasp of the whole, a two-fold process which is by nature indeterminate.

However, is it not necessary to fix on a central point in terms of which the whole becomes intelligible? This question brings us back to the problem, which we shall develop later, of historical units. At this point, let us note a simple but fundamental fact: nothing proves that there is *one* interpretation of a man, sect, society, era, which is uniquely valid, or more valid than others.

Consider this plurality of possibilities in trying to understand *one* person. Perhaps the psychoanalyst can, after long research, establish the psychic history of an individual. But the life-history of Gide, as told by the psychoanalyst, is not necessarily the most profound or instructive interpretation of his work and thought. When dealing with many men—sects, parties, epochs, societies—it is doubtful that psychoanalytic interpretation achieves the same degree of probability as in the case of an individual analysis. In any case, such interpretation would be only moderately instructive for the historian. Understanding the ideological universe of the Bolsheviks is more instructive for him than insight (equivocal, uncertain) into the psychological mechanisms which have contributed to the Bolshevik mode of thinking and acting.

Is not understanding the mental universe of the Bolsheviks a task which confronts historians of twentieth-century Russia? Is not understanding the mental universe of the fifth-century Athenians a task confronting historians of ancient Greece? And is not this understanding by its very nature incomplete, always susceptible to deepening and to further precision? Uniform interpretation does not exist in knowledge, perhaps because unity of the governing principle (*principe formateur*) does not exist in reality. Human reality is, by nature, equivocal. One man's idea of another depends on what they both are. Mutual understanding between men is essentially a dialogue, an exchange.

The scientific effort of the historian tends not to suppress this element of dialogue but to eliminate the arbitrary, the incorrect, and the partial. The global interpretation of humanity always contains some measure of inference, but such interpretation is scientific when it takes account of *all* the data. The historian does not become scientific by de-personalizing himself but by submitting his personality to the rigors of criticism and the standards of proof. He never offers a definitive image of the past but, sometimes, he offers definitively *one* valid image of it.

The second question—why and how an event is produced—is that of historical determinism. Actually, to consider a certain fact as an event is to admit the possibility that it did not occur (at least not on a given date). We investigate the causes of the Austro-Hungarian ultimatum to Serbia or the European war of 1914, because the ultimatum and the war are the results of decisions taken by certain men, decisions which do not seem to have been inevitable. The search for laws in the natural, or even behavioral, sciences postulates the determinism which it strives to elaborate. The search for causes, in history and especially human history, presupposes contingency (which does not mean indeterminism), i.e., the appearance at a point in time and space of a datum which was not the necessary result of laws. The automobile which skids off the road and is thrown against a tree moves in conformity with the laws of nature; but the braking, caused by an approaching pedestrian, might very well not have taken place.

On the microscopic level, when we seek the causes of an event involving one or many men, causation is often confused with intention, with the actor's purpose, with the rational considerations or the passions which led him to act. No historian would retrace the origins of the war without concern for the psycho-historical personages. Every book about the days and weeks preceding the explosion of

August 2, 1914, interprets the conduct of each personage, trying to grasp his intentions as well as his actions. But this investigation, similar to that of a court of inquiry, has two aspects: either we refer to what took place in the minds of men, or we seek the causes and trace the consequences. These two aspects of inquiry are logically distinct.

Did the ministers of Vienna think that Serbia would submit to the ultimatum? Did they think that Russia would not intervene if Austro-Hungary were to give a military lesson to little Serbia? These questions concern the motives behind the actions, the horizon in view of which a certain decision was taken. The historian is right to ask what were the probable consequences of the ultimatum at the time, and what were the chances of localizing the conflict. The discrepancy between the actor's expectation and the historian's analysis can gauge the error or willful illusion of the former. Further, the historian tries to determine in what measure the decision (the ultimatum, the declaration of war) was the necessary outcome of the circumstances, or was derived from an action not implied by the situation. Given an event, the historian goes back to the past to establish to what extent it was the inevitable outcome of that which went before, then proceeds into the future to trace the consequences of that which may have been the voluntary act of a single individual.

What is the sense of this kind of inquiry? Our example suggests it. Suppose we conclude with the proposition that the ultimatum sent by the Vienna Cabinet to Serbia would have made a local war and thus, by the play of alliances, a European war almost inevitable: we would thus have isolated the immediate "cause" of the explosion. The sufficiency of that cause has nothing to do with the legitimacy or illegitimacy of the demands made on Serbia. One can say that these demands were legitimate (by reason of the complicity of certain Serbian military men in the assassination at Sarajevo) and yet say, all the same, that Serbia's semi-negative reply and Russia's intervention had been politically predictable and inevitable.

One may ask on what the answers to such specific questions can be based. Are we here dealing with data or with hypotheses? What are the available facts? What are the possible inferences? In vain would we look for irrefutable proof at the microscopic level on which we chose our example. What we know is that before the Austro-Hungarian ultimatum was sent, Europe did not fear an imminent explosion, but after the ultimatum all the chancelleries judged a general war possible if not probable. The facts justifying this statement are: the severity of the conditions formulated in the ultimatum, and the system of alliances which scarcely permitted a limited conflict. The disagreements among historians concern either the intentions of the ministers at Vienna, or the legitimacy of the Austrian demands, or finally the probability of war after the ultimatum. The degree of probability is confused, so to speak, with the degree of causality. We can set aside the question of the degree of probability: the event occurred only once and we can imagine, but not know, what would have happened if it had not occurred. It is of no consequence to seek an absolute certainty contrary to the nature of reality and to the nature of our knowledge.

The aim of causal inquiry, as we have shown in a particular case, is to reveal the structure of the course of history, to disentangle the skein of great underlying causes and particular events. As for the immediate causes of the war, it seems to me that scientific study has demonstrated the essential point: the war was born of a "diplomatic failure." No government had a clear and strong desire for a general war, none rejected the likelihood. The initial risk was taken by the Austrian government, which had been promised support by Germany. Discussion revolves around the legitimacy of the Austrian demands, the haste with which St. Petersburg and Paris responded, and the hesitations of London. The facts permit us to rediscover the interweaving of initiatives and necessities, of accidents and determinants, which comprise the drama of human history and which the historian's curiosity seeks to reconstitute.

Such inquiry rarely unfolds on the microscopic level at which we have placed ourselves. The immediate origins of an event are not often so obscure that they require a scientific deciphering. But at a higher level we find an analogous question. Many historians consider research on the immediate causes of the war of 1914 devoid of interest because, in their view, it would have happened in any case. Scientifically, one cannot choose between immediate and long-range causes; either or both may attract the attention of the historian. But if he is convinced that the latter made an event *inevitable,* then study of the former loses all importance. *If* the European situation in 1914 was such that any incident could have touched off the spark, then the cause lay almost entirely in the situation and the incident was no more than an occasion for action.

Again, the question is: how can such propositions be proved? And again, the answer is that irrefutable proof is impossible. We cannot repeat the experiment, eliminate the incident of July 1914, so that history may take another course—which might confirm or refute the hypothesis of "inevitability." All we can do is to perform mental experiments. We try to combine the fundamental data of the situation with a variety of accidents to conclude that in the largest number of cases (or in all, or in only a few) the event would have occurred. The inference is drawn from the facts but it goes beyond them.

How accurate are such inferences? I do not think that we can risk a generalization. Given the European situation after Munich, it seems to me that to avoid the war of 1939 would have required a fundamental modification of the Hitler regime. In other words, from the end of 1938, war was inevitable barring unlikely accidents (sudden death of Hitler, successful plot against him, etc.) In 1914, the situation was precarious and most observers considered war likely. But the date at least was uncertain and the date, in turn, could have had long-range consequences. Had war broken out in 1920 or in 1925, would it have taken the same course and produced the same results?

These sorts of judgments on the causes of what is past by mental confrontation with a possible and unreal alternative course are to the past what forecasts are to the future. That an event intervened effectively we know only after it has taken place, but we do not know whether it was the effect of the situation, considered in its main outlines, or of some incident due to an individual or to a connected series. Hence, when we assert a causal relation between a situation and a past event, our assertion is no more indisputable than is the forecast of such an event. (The judgment that an event occurred is indisputable. The judgment that it was the effect solely of a given situation is not indisputable.)

Judgments about historical causality drawn from imaginary comparisons between what occurred and what might have occurred can take many forms: 1) Judgments of sufficient causality; a situation makes an event inevitable. 2) Judgments of accidental causality; the event was not determined by a situation, but was provoked by a detail, accident, or person. Obviously these two kinds of judgments are complementary: if the European situation in October 1938 made a European war inevitable soon, of what importance are the final incidents and the behavior of diplomats here and there? 3) Judgments attributing to an event or person the role of *initiator*: e.g., the Austro-

Hungarian ultimatum is the prime mover in the course that led to the war of 1914, the Bolshevik seizure of power in 1917 is the prime mover in the course which spread Communism over half the globe. 4) Judgments attributing to an event or person a "reversal" or "regressive effect" in relation to the trend preceding it: e.g., the political evolution of Europe in the direction of liberal institutions was arrested and turned back by the war of 1914; the Bolshevik Party turned the evolution of European socialism away from peaceful methods. Does the Soviet regime continue or divert the ancient course of Russian history, which had for several decades been moving towards more liberal or constitutional procedures? 5) Judgments attributing to a person responsibility for the particular characteristics of a movement or regime (which may have been inevitable in some form). If we suppose that the revolutionary crisis made a military dictatorship inevitable or very probable, in what respect did Napoleon's own genius leave its mark on France and Europe? If we suppose that after Lenin's death the absolute power of one individual was inevitable or very probable, what aspects of the Soviet regime were determined by the special features of Stalin, "the man of steel"?

All such judgments are logically, of the same kind. They illustrate how the much-discussed problems of the role of Great Men, of determinism and accident, manifest themselves. These problems are not philosophical but scientific. They are concerned not with values but with facts. Differences bear on degree rather than principle. No one claims that, with another man in Napoleon's or Stalin's place, nothing would have been changed in France between 1789 and 1815, in Russia between 1924 and 1953. Neither does anyone assert that Napoleon and Stalin would have acted in exactly the same ways had they ruled in different countries. Great Men alter something, but they cannot alter everything.

What can they alter? The answer cannot be formulated in general terms. The margin of influence for Great Men is larger or smaller depending on the epoch. It can never be measured exactly with certainty. What would the Soviet regime have been without Stalin? No one can say in detail, but one can say that it is not demonstrated that such phenomena as the great purge would have occurred if the Party Secretary had been Trotsky or Bukharin. If we object that neither of them had a chance to succeed, it remains that the man capable of success did not have to posses the psychological peculiarities which were the cause of certain aspects of the Soviet regime (forced confessions, purges, etc.). Scientifically, Stalin's decisive influence is established when the impossibility of denying it is demonstrated. How should we reconstitute Russia of the Five-Year Plans without Stalin, or with another leader? No one can say, whatever the powers of his imagination. But it suffices that certain phenomena are not necessarily bound to the economic-political-social situation in order for Stalin's personality to appear as their possible cause and to take on, at least hypothetically, the appearance of an historical force.

The limits on proof explain the divergence of theories and judgments. Since the impact of the individual cannot be ruled out, some observers assert it categorically: a general less ambitious and gifted than Napoleon Bonaparte would not have used the forces of revolutionary France to overrun Europe; a despot less suspicious and cruel than Stalin would not have added to the unavoidable hardships of the Five-Year Plans, the merciless suppression of the peasant revolts and the elimination of Lenin's comrades in the theatrical setting of the trials. Other observers incline to the opposite view: in the same situation another man, for social or psychological reasons, would have been driven to the same excesses. According to the case, one theory or the other seems more likely, the degree of individual responsibility greater or smaller. Logically, what has been established is the impossibility of proving the ineffectiveness of an individual or event, which results in the probability more or less great that a role more or less important, according to the circumstances, is played by a person or event.

The discussion is considerably more important when it concerns causality in the initiation of a series. In the absence of Lenin and Trotsky, would the Bolshevik Revolution have succeeded? If the Bolshevik Party had not triumphed, would a fundamentally different evolution (industrial progress under a democratic regime) have been possible? That is, would it have been compatible with the basic data of the Russian situation? The data do not permit categorical answers to either of these questions. Any hypothesis about the responsibility of two men in the success of a party, even more any hypothesis about the possible evolution of non-Bolshevik Russia, is hazardous, at best. Since the relative probability of different hypotheses is subject to dispute, so historians select resolutely according to their preferences. One recounts history in such a way that things could not have happened otherwise than they did. Another, telling the same story, emphasizes what seems to him ascribable to individuals and what, with a few details altered, could have happened (e.g., a non-Bolshevik Russia).

These extreme theories, by their very opposition, reveal the structure of historical reality. Historical necessity, or what we call by that name, expresses itself only in the men who are its agents and interpreters. When two sides offer themselves equally as interpreters of necessity, the event alone decides between them. If the event is still to come, we despair of forecasting it. Why then, looking back, should we claim that we could have forecast the event, i.e., that the situation predetermined the outcome? Perhaps certain men, or a fortunate or unfortunate happening, swung the balance to one side or the other. When many persons seek to be the agents of necessity we, the contemporaries, do not think that anything will be changed by the victor's name. Why apply to the past a criterion different from what we apply to the present and to the future?

The problem of historical determinism, as I have sketched it, is basically one of action and necessity. He who sees the course of history ruled solely by the compulsion of supra-individual forces eliminates the actions of individuals. He who sees the course of history as determined, at every moment, by unforeseeable events rules out all comprehensive intelligibility and thus implies chaos. The historian preoccupied with determinism strives to grasp the dramatic character of history as defined by the dialectic of men and their milieux, of necessities and accidents.

To suppress one of the two terms of the dialectic, one must place oneself high above events and, in the manner of the philosopher or the theologian, retain only that which marks a stage in the progress of the self-made universe of man. Or, by contrast, one must plunge into the thick of events and, like the true man of action, place almost unlimited confidence in the human will, leaving all the rest to fortune. The historian is neither the man of action nor the philosopher: retaining both terms, he investigates how that happened which holds the attention only of the philosopher, how the will of the actors, destiny, and accident have conspired in the realization of something not foreseen or desired by anyone, but ultimately the act and experience of all.

III

Philosophers, historians, or logicians who have reflected on the reconstruction of human events have all been struck by the contrast between the apparent incoherence of history as it is lived and the orderliness of history as it is retold. The most familiar example is battle. What took place one day in June, 1815, on a Belgian plain, is what we call the Battle of Waterloo. In what did the reality of the battle consist? Thousands and thousands of men thought, acted, lived, were wounded, and died. Is the reality composed of the movements of individuals? These movements are without meaning if they are observed from outside, abstracted from the thoughts of the persons who made them. The reality lies in the connections between the movements and the states of consciousness, the latter imparting meaning to the former. But who creates the unity of these countless thoughts and movements? The material unity is one of place and time: the battle began at a certain hour in the morning, at a particular spot, and also ended at a point in space and time. But this spatio-temporal unit is strictly material (and even in this respect it is imperfect; the action was prolonged until which moment, to what point?). The states of consciousness are an integral part of the reality: whence comes their unity, that which is called the Battle of Waterloo? Logically, the answer is that historical unity is not experienced, but constructed.

Novelists who describe the battle as lived through by a simple cavalryman seek to show the contrast between the battle experience of an individual combatant and the stylized representation given by historians. The contrast exists, but it does not signify that the individual combatant's experience of the battle is the reality, while the historian's representation is fiction. The *ensemble* makes no sense to the man who knows only a fragment: it is nonetheless *real* for him who does grasp its unity and its internal texture.

At what level does the historian try to understand the battle? Everything depends on the orientation of his curiosity. If he is interested in its tactical development, he will concentrate on details. If he is more interested in the skill of the leaders, he will start with the plans of the two commanding generals. At each level—that of the individual combatant and that of the strategist—he will discover a pattern intelligible in terms of plans of one man or many.

A battle, although it is not an atom, is no less an historical fact. Is this fact to be related to the vaster units of nation, period, culture? Are historical units always of the same kind? If there are essential differences among them, where do the important distinctions lie?

Let us begin with a banal but not meaningless remark: the Battle of Waterloo, in the eyes of the historian, must be placed in a larger context. How are we to understand the organization of the French army and its conduct under fire, without turning to the past—to the rise of the revolutionary armies, their transformation, and then to the disintegration of the imperial armies. The French and English soldiers who faced each other on the Belgian plains were the product of a long series of battles, of victories, and defeats, which had formed, weakened, or hardened both sides. And if we turn from Waterloo to the armies of the Revolution we must go back even further, to the royal armies, and so on, indefinitely.

Let us be clear that we do not mean that, to understand or explain what took place on June 18, 1815, we must know what in the French army could be ascribed to monarchical tradition. But the historian is not content merely to describe the event: he wishes to discover its origins: he searches for its causes in the past. Since he is interested in *how* things occur, he cannot help following a chronological order because each moment is the heir of the one which preceded it, and takes its significance only in the light of past events. This need to enlarge the inquiry little by little on which Toynbee after so many others has insisted, does not result only from the continuity of human history, from the presence here and now of institutions and ideas whose origins are lost in the dark reaches of time. It is born also of historical curiosity. The historian of Paris, as an historian, neither can nor will stop before Lutèce. The sociologist can and must set limits to temporal regression.

When we pass from "the Battle of Waterloo" to the "Wars of the Revolution and the Empire," have we changed species? The spatio-temporal unity of the wars of the Empire is less clearly marked than that of the "Battle of Waterloo," but it is not fundamentally different. These wars had a beginning and end in time, and they had a specifiable scene of action. It is true that a man was able, perhaps at a glance, to take in the whole of a battle, while the *ensemble* of the wars of the Revolution and the Empire can only be a construct of his mind. But, on this view, the battle of the Marne in September 1914, by virtue of its geographical dimensions, belongs to the species "war" and not "battle." It eludes the sensory grasp of a single individual.

In the Battle of Waterloo, spatial-temporal unity interacts with the unity of design arranged by the two commanders-in-chief. The event did not correspond exactly to either of the two plans but their two minds had attempted to shape the event before it took place. The case is different with the wars of the Revolution and the Empire, which clearly no one could have conceived in advance. The difference is not insignificant, but it is not, I believe, decisive. Many isolated events—the fall of the Bastille, the taking of the Tuileries on August 10—were really not thought of in advance by anyone. They were not the result of the conscious desire of an individual, but of the countless deeds, words, and acts of many people. However, the historian is not mistaken in seeing here an "historical unity" if these events have had the world-wide consequences to which their contemporaries testify and historical study confirms.

To the extent that we consider larger *ensembles,* the two elementary factors of historical unity (spatio-temporal unity, and the unity of one or more human plans) disappear, but unity does not therefore become pure fiction. We speak of the "Wars of the Revolution and the Empire" because the Revolution of 1789 set off a cycle of conflicts caused principally by the questioning of traditional political regimes and the transformation of armies. France's return to its former size and to a monarchical regime marked the end of it. We speak legitimately of these wars as a unity because despite their duration and diversity, they derive their coherence and significance from a small number of causes.

The historians who try to handle the great periods of history seek both the facts which dominated each epoch and those which provoked the ruptures with tradition. The "periodization" of history is the result of a legitimate intention. It remains to be seen at what point the data demonstrate the validity of the division into any such periods. We have already mentioned one of the best known "periodizations," that of economic history set forth by Marx in the introduction to *The Critique of Political Economy,* which serializes world history as primitive communism, the Asiatic mode of production, the slave economy of antiquity, the serf economy of the middle ages, the wage economy of modern capitalism, and the socialism of tomorrow. The principle of this "periodization" is the dependence of men on their work. The schema would be absolutely valid if, in each period, everything differed with respect to this predominant factor. The criterion would in this case be linked to a cause which, above all others, was the determinant of the rest of society. But the criterion would be insignificant if it were a secondary phenomenon. The criteria chosen by historians always lie between these two extremes. They were neither exclusive cause nor trivial datum.

The dependence of man on work, exemplified in the concept of the wage-earner, is not inconsequential. The error begins when the historian decides arbitrarily that the existence of a wage-earning class necessarily excludes certain changes, such as the raising of the standard of living or the improvement of human relations between employer and employed. The polemical use of the word "capitalism" is bound to an error of this sort. Capitalism, having been defined with reference to the wage-earner, is declared to be bad and beyond reform. To ask what reforms are possible within the framework of capitalism is to ask what positive or negative consequences are required by the fact chosen as criterion of this economic regime, the class of wage-earners in the present case. It is possible to show that certain changes are not impeded by the existence of this class; further, that some changes are determined by technological or economic evolution, and do not require the disappearance of this class.

The lesson we wish to draw from this example is not that the historian must abandon his efforts to establish periods, or to characterize a period by a fact which he considers of special importance. The lesson is more complex. The historian has a certain freedom in the choice of criteria which he may use to characterize a period. But he is not at liberty to attribute to his choice a significance which only empirical investigation can confer. The economist can decide that the relation of men to work interests him above all else; he may decide that there is a great difference between subordination to an entrepreneur and to the State; but he must examine the facts of the standard of living, the physical or moral conditions of the worker, to demonstrate, and not simply postulate or imagine, the consequence of the alleged differences.

Let us go one step further. What are we to think of those vast units which Spengler has called *cultures* and Toynbee *societies* or *civilizations?* Are they realities, or are they nothing more than a figment of the historical imagination? The preceding analyses have illustrated the relative character of the idea of reality as applied to the historical world. Materially, only individuals are real. But historical reality is not material. It consists of experiences or meanings produced by these experiences, meanings which transcend individual consciousness. Human conduct sometimes exhibits an order and a coherence, which none of the actors ever conceived or desired. The intelligibility of historical meanings is not microscopic, and we cannot exclude *a priori* the reality of immense civilizations.

But this reality is not self-evident either; it can only result from inquiry. Cultures, in Spengler's sense, are the more real when: 1) there is no communication between them; 2) they have clearly defined spatial-temporal limits; 3) they present an internal coherence attributable to one sufficient cause; 4) they are essentially original in comparison to other cultures. Spengler did not hesitate to declare that each culture, inspired by a unique spirit, was basically incapable of change, each being self-contained and bearing in all its aspects the sign of its incomparable purpose—and each eventually following in its turn the same stages of a destined course.

Toynbee does not go so far. Civilizations emerge from each other, they leave their mark upon each other, they are not fundamentally incomprehensible to one another. But the closer Toynbee comes to the facts, the less convincing he is about the reality of civilizations. He begins by opposing them to nations on the pretext that they, not the latter, prove "an intelligible field of study." But civilizations of the second generation cannot be understood without reference to the parent civilization. If these civilizations do not possess clearly drawn and self-sufficient limits, they ought to have coherence and originality. Whence does each derive its originality? Toynbee suggests that religion constitutes the principle of originality, but he does not say so distinctly, he does not prove it, he does not even insist on originality itself. Not one of the four aspects of reality which we have enumerated is incontestably present in Toynbee's civilizations: they communicate with each other, they have no clearly defined boundaries in time and space, no clearly revealed coherence or originality. Do they have at least a typical evolution which permits us to recognize them as species of the same genus? We dare not say so, when the "universal empire" can occur one thousand years late (civilization of Oriental Christianity), or when a "petrified" civilization sees its "typical evolution" interrupted for a very long time.

Does nothing remain of Toynbee's conception of the plurality of civilizations? We would not go that far. There remains the plurality of value systems, of collective organizations, or religious beliefs. In this sense, history is not monolithic. What is still in question is the degree of separation between civilizations and the degree of coherence of each. Once the Spenglerian dogmatism of radical impermeability and singularity is rejected, there still exist indisputable differences in ways of life, thought, belief, and the organization of this diversity in a small number of patterns which are neither pure imagination nor irrefutable evidence.

The error originates when, departing from the facts which prove the diversity and the equivocal reality of *ensembles,* one infers a kind of metaphysics which transforms these *ensembles* into living beings, fated to be born and to die.

In a longer analysis, we would consider all types of historical units. But we would confront problems similar to those we have sketched: the reality of historical units is ambiguous, for the facts suggest them but rarely impose them. Logically, the historian must never forget the nature of the unit he reconstructs, and he must not attribute to a mode of understanding a causal significance which it does not possess. It is experience, not intuition or reason, which shows what variations can take place in an *ensemble* defined by a precise criterion.

IV

Just as historical units are in some way connected with the understanding of the actors, patterns of change are somehow connected with the question of how and why. Rarely do patterns of change lack a more or less explicit interpretation of the causes which determine them.

In the history of historical thinking, the notion of cycles is perhaps the oldest and most familiar. Political philosophers since Plato and Aristotle have many times described or imagined the succession of regimes (monarchy, aristocracy, democracy degenerating into a demogogy, which produces a tyranny that constitutes the origin of a new cycle). Perhaps they have recognized in the course of human history an equivalent of the revolution of the stars, of great cosmic cycles which are themselves more often imagined than observed. Nietzsche had the intuition of the eternal return, which extended to the entire universe and to each event the pitiless and perhaps comforting law of repetition.

The scientific historian does not have to choose between varied schemas of change, between cycles and progress, but he inevitably meets problems inseparable from these schemas. *The nature of changes and their pattern is the essence of human activity ana its accomplished works.* The meaning of history is inseparable from the works whose history we trace. A schema of change results from the relationship of two moments in time. The relationship of two events—e.g., peace in Europe and imperialist onslaught in Africa—

may be that of succession, of causality, or of simple coincidence. Imperialism may translate the response of diplomats, officers, or people to continental peace. But the relationship varies with the events under consideration, and only empirical inquiry can clarify its real nature in each case. Let us suppose that we are interested in the relationship between two works of art or between two mathematical truths. The relationship as such will be essentially different because the works as such have different meaning. The statuary of Phidias, of the cathedral at Reims, of the Elephanta caves will never be organized into a system in the manner of mathematical theorems or physical laws. The history of art, as art, is that of diverse creations; the history of mathematics is that of the elaboration of a system.

Let us repeat that these propositions concern the works as such. Every creation was first the result or expression of consciousness and the history of scientific discovery is no more ordained than is that of artistic creation. There have been periods of stagnation and others of movement, of advance, and of retreat. On the level of men and events, the patterns of the history of the sciences is no more known in advance than is the history of political regimes or of artistic styles. The history of the sciences can be considered progress to the extent that we isolate proven truths from the philosophical or ideological trappings in which they first appear, to the extent that we make an abstraction of the social conditions which favored or impeded discovery. If we can think of the history of art as the development of pure diversity, it is to the extent that we isolate the individual work in its beauty from the technical means that were indispensable to its creation and from the style of which it partakes as the result of a long apprenticeship. The essence of true scientific propositions is that they are cumulative and, often, organized into a system. The essence of beautiful things is to succeed one another, each unique and irreplaceable.

When the very nature of the work is equivocal or lends itself to many interpretations, the meaning of history takes on the same indeterminacy. Philosophy is the outstanding example of this. Is philosophy in each epoch the rigorous formulation of a certain vision of the world? If this is its intrinsic meaning, then its history is inseparable from general history, for it reflects in an intellectually elaborated fashion the idea that each epoch and each people has had of itself. To other philosophers, on the contrary, this history of world views remains external to the essence of philosophical inquiry, because these visions of the world are stripped of the pretension to truth which no philosopher voluntarily renounces. *Philosophie als strenge Wilsenschaft* and *Psychologie der Weltsanschaugen*, Husserl and Dilthey, mark the two extreme positions between which other interpretations can be found. In the view of positivistic logic, the history of philosophy is the progressive discovery of those questions which have meaning and those which do not; in the view of the Hegelian (or Marxist), the history of philosophy reflects both the successive phases of human consciousness and the stages of progression toward total truth.

The historian of a particular sphere subscribes more or less consciously to a theory of his sphere—a theory more often borrowed from the philosopher than from the historian. It is not that the theory can be proved independently of historical data, but that these data never impose a theory or, at any rate, impose it only on condition of their being deciphered in a certain manner. For our problem, we need only recall that determination of the real nature of a work and the specific meaning of its history cannot be based exclusively on factual data or experimental induction. It requires a properly philosophical argumentation.

Relating the patterns of change (progress, cycle, diversity) not to the essence of a particular history, but to events, is a logically simple problem. It is a matter of questioning the facts without dictating their response. Logic decrees in the first place not to give events a constant orientation in dealing with the specific meaning of an activity. For example, the history of technology is one of progress; it does not therefore follow that the technology of a society will progress continuously or that a society like ours, which is conscious and desirous of such progress, will not experience periods of stagnation or even, in the event of an atomic catastrophe, of regression.

Beyond this, it is necessary to fix exact limits to the validity of schemas of change for a given period and sector. For example, the last half-century has seen extension of the state's functions and the reduction of the zone in which individual initiatives come into play. It would be dangerous to extrapolate indefinitely a trend of this sort. The arrest and reversal of such a trend are conceivable. In any case, if one infers from the facts the indefinite continuation of this trend, the inference must be justified not only by a statement of the past trend but by analysis of the facts which make it inevitable. Historical extrapolations are most often hazardous because they bear on a limited area without cognizance of the complexity of historical reality, and without noting forces contrary to those which move in the extrapolated direction. In the place of a history which tends always toward one meaning, one should put the presentation of a struggle between relatively autonomous forces whose outcome is not decided in advance. The image of conflict seems to me preferable to the image of a river.

Patterns of change are most often bound to the formation of historical units. The traditional example of change, which we cited at the beginning of this section, is that of the cycle of governmental forms. The Marxist thesis also implies the formation of historical units, specified by the single variable of man's dependence on work. Such a pattern is worth what the historical units themselves are worth. If the organization of the English textile industry at the beginning of the nineteenth century, which Marx studied, is subsumed under the same concept of capitalism that includes the great American corporations of the mid-twentieth century, the historical unit has little significance because the allegedly determinant variable is diffuse. But if we suppose that man's dependence on work disappears when the private entrepreneur is replaced by the state, then the transition from capitalism to socialism, proclaimed as inevitable, would be of as little significance as the simple nationalization of corporations. This inference cannot be proved, for in no country where partial socialization has been achieved has this involved or seemed to imply total socialization.

There remains, finally, one type of pattern of change on which we may comment. Can we observe or infer a certain pattern applicable to all of human history? The encompassing of historical totality admits, logically, of two methods: either we relate the whole to the one aspect of human existence which we judge to be decisive in the realm of values and not of effects; or we analyze the totality in such a way as to determine the internal structure and the dominant variables by which we can explain past phases and predict future phases. These two modes are frequently confused or only poorly differentiated. In Marxism, is economic activity essential because it determines all else or because labor is the whole meaning of life? Marxists waver between the two alternatives in the hope that both are correct.

The theology of history is the pure example of the apprehension of the totality in relation to what alone matters: salvation, the relation of mankind to God the Creator. A philosophy such as Spengler's or Sorokin's, perhaps Toynbee's, belongs to this category. Cultures, in Spengler's sense, are the units animated by a fundamental purpose, and the interpretation of each culture according to its purpose would be true because it would correspond to reality. Theology of history and philosophy of cultures both pretend to the truth, but the truth of the former is one with the religion which it proclaims, whereas the truth of the latter rests on the facts by which it claims to be proved.

True or false, the philosophy of cultures cannot refute a theology of history—the interpretation of history by reference to the religious calling of humanity—but this observation applies also to the secularized versions of the theology of history. The philosopher who believes that history realizes its vocation in the discovery of scientific truth will relate all cultures (even if Spengler is correct) to this major activity which defines the essence of man. He will discover a pattern of change different from that of the historian who wishes to put all the diverse activities of man on the same level.

But, as we have already seen, the reality of historical units as vast as cultures is always equivocal. Cultures are never entirely unified, either by the predominant action of a single cause or by the logic of a system of ideas and values. In one way, the repetition of the same pattern of change would confirm the existence of multiple and original cultures. The similarity of phases traversed is often disputable. If Toynbee finds everywhere "warrior states" and "the universal empire," it is because these concepts are formalized to the point where they denote simply the existence of rival sovereignties and imperial unification. Also, one must sometimes wait a thousand years for a universal empire that is late for its rendezvous.

*   *   *

The question of patterns of change reviews the problematical in the three preceding problems while leading us from the science to the philosophy of history.

Patterns relating to a partial sector over a limited time are inseparable from an analysis of "why" and of historical units. The more we succeed in clarifying the proposition that if certain partial data had been otherwise the course of history would have been something else, the more we dispose of the fiction of an inevitable future; that fiction is created by illegitimate extrapolations from a limited trend, by the neglect of concurrent forces, of possible events, of acting men. As for schemas which set forth the succession of historical units, they cannot be worth more than the units they bind together. The proclamation of inevitable socialism cannot signify more than the definition of socialism. The socialism which can be claimed to be inevitable is, it seems to me, closer to Western capitalism than to the Soviet regime. The socialism defined by the characteristics of the present Communist regime is not inevitable.

Beyond these patterns of a sector, we examine those schemas related to the whole. But here we come back to the initial question (understanding of men) at the same time that we by-pass all scientific examination. The meaning of the history of an activity is bound to the essential nature of that activity. The meaning of "total" history is the meaning which we attach to human existence and to the succession of forms that it takes through time.

Is man in search of something—salvation of the soul, the truth in nature or in himself? Or is he merely a beast of prey, fated to remain such, gratuitously and vainly creating cultures, all unique, and all doomed to die? There is no need to answer these questions or to choose among the answers in order scientifically to reconstitute the past. But, subtly, these answers do influence the way in which each historian reconstructs the past. The historical *ensemble* is neither juxtaposition nor complete coherence: we can analyze its texture without rigorously separating the analysis from the hierarchy of values established between the activities and the works of man. Logically, the philosophy of history is detached from science to the extent that it interprets total history, i.e., to the extent that it gives, explicitly or not, an answer to the question man asks himself in questioning his past. The historical experience does not give an answer; rather the experience which we draw from the past is prescribed by an implicit answer which we carry in us before we question those who have been.

In our time, the purpose of industrial societies is convincingly inscribed in the monuments of steel as well as in the declarations of statesmen: mastery of natural forces to assure to all men honorable conditions of existence. But do the garden cities spread over the surface of the earth give men the feeling of having attained the limits of their quest and their adventure? Certainly too many possible catastrophes, too much real misery forbid us to worry about what the happy citizens would do in the state where abundance reigned.

It would not be less fallacious to imagine that abundance satisfies all our doubts than to believe abundance inevitable under one economic regime or another. Uncertainty about the future is tied to the limitations of our verifiable knowledge and to the complexity of reality—to the uncertainty of meaning of the problematical in humanity itself.

Evidence and Inference in the Law

Henry M. Hart, Jr., and John T. McNaughton

The central difficulty in a discussion of evidence and inference in the law is that the law has no single technique for connecting its conclusions with supporting data. The problems are highly varied, and techniques of decision vary correspondingly. A unified account of "evidence and inference in the law" is thus impossible. What we have chosen to do in the face of this difficulty is to select for discussion three major types of problems, to give examples of each, and to try to indicate in relation to each some of the important ways in which legal problems differ from problems in other disciplines.

First, however, a word should be said about the nature of the law generally, and about the distinctive character which all legal problems have by virtue of the fact that they are concerned with the administration of the law. It is useful to think of the law as comprising a system of authoritative general directions telling people what they can, may, or must do, and, sometimes, what will happen if they do otherwise. But, as we must stress from the outset, many of these directions are highly uncertain and indeterminate. The system, therefore, includes various kinds of auxiliary directions telling how such uncertainties are to be resolved when an occasion for resolution arises.

At the heart of the system in its everyday functioning are those directions which speak directly to private persons, requiring them to decide in the first instance what the directions mean and whether or not to comply with them. For example: "Do not commit murder." "Pay your income tax." "Do not libel or slander anyone." "If you wish to make a valid will, do it this way." "Carry out your duly made contracts." "This is the way to form a corporation."

Accompanying or underlying these privately addressed directions are others addressed in the first instance to various kinds of officials. Some of these directions tell officials, such as police and prosecuting attorneys and courts, what to do if directions of the first type are not complied with, or are thought not to have been complied with. Others are addressed to various types of executive and administrative officials, telling them how to build roads or to administer a system of social security or to carry out any of the innumerable regulatory and non-regulatory activities in which modern governments engage. Still others, embodied chiefly in constitutions, are addressed to legislatures, telling them how to formulate these and other kinds of authoritative general directions in the first place.

Characteristics of Legal Directions

Five points are especially to be noted about legal directions of all types.

1. They deal with important matters. Immediately or remotely, they touch almost all the concerns of human life, from the most trivial to the most deeply felt. They shape the very structure of the social order, from which flow all the pleasures and pains of social living.

2. Legal directions are authoritative. They speak with the power and prestige of the community behind them. At stake in their administration, therefore, is the good name as well as the good order of the community; and these are, of course, closely related.

3. Legal directions speak over a period of time, and characteristically over long periods. At the moment of their making, they speak from the present to the future. At the moment of their application, they speak out of the past to the present. The difficulties of discerning what the past has to say to the present are great. The difficulties of deciding what the present can wisely try to say to the future are even greater. These difficulties explain why so often it is not only necessary but desirable that the directions should be in some measure indeterminate.

4. Legal directions always contemplate the subsuming of particulars under previously established generals. Their application always involves the double task of ascertaining the general which is to be applied and of identifying the particulars which make it applicable. In few, if any, other disciplines is a problem of this dual type encountered. In most other disciplines, the generalizations are drawn from the facts and are controlled by them. The generalizations of the law, in contrast, are prescriptive rather than descriptive.

5. Legal directions, finally, are the expressions of human purposes. This, of course, is the reason why they can never be deduced,

simply, from the particulars to which they are applied. The physical environment of human life and the physical and psychological facts of human nature fix the conditions under which human purposes must be pursued. They set limits, therefore, upon the purposes which are realizable. But they do not predetermine the purposes which *ought* to be or which *will* be realized. If there is such a thing as a "behavioral science," in other words, law is not one of them. Law exists to shape human behavior, but is also shaped by it. It is a science not only of what is but of what ought to be. This inescapably purposive character of law pervades and colors every legal problem.

Now to the three selected problems: the first emphasizes primarily the *applying* of legal directions, the second the *elaborating* of legal directions, and the third the *making* of legal directions.

I. THE AFTER-THE-EVENT DETERMINATION OF ADJUDICATIVE FACTS

The first type of problem we have chosen is the simplest. It is the problem presented when a tribunal is called upon to apply a legal direction of undisputed content to a disputed state of fact. Ordinarily, such a direction will be a legal "rule" in the technical sense. Such a rule can be defined as an authoritative general direction which requires for its application only a determination of the happening or non-happening of physical or mental events. In logical terms, the rule is a special kind—a "prescriptive" kind—of major premise; the conclusion follows if the propositions comprising the minor premise are proved. While such a minor premise may include a proposition that something is likely to happen in the future, generally the problem is one of determining historical facts.

Illustrative Cases

Here are typical examples of simple undisputed-law, disputed-fact cases:

(1) A man is charged with murder. The rule made relevant by the facts of the case may be that any sane person who with malice aforethought kills another person shall be put to death. The facts are such that there are no difficult questions of definition, say, of "sane" or of "malice aforethought." The only question is whether

it was the defendant who fired the fatal shot. (2) A man is sued for breach of warranty. The rule made applicable by the facts of the situation may be that any person who sells goods to another which are not up to the seller's representations shall, provided the buyer gives prompt notice of the defect, pay the buyer a sum of money equal to the difference between the value of the goods promised and of those delivered. The facts raise no doubts as to the exact meaning of the rule. The only issue is whether the goods delivered were as represented by the seller. (3) A large estate is to be distributed. The relevant rule may be that two-thirds of the estate of any person dying without a will shall be divided equally among his children. There are no close questions requiring the law of descent to be clarified. The only question is whether the claimant is or is not one of the children of the deceased.

In such simple situations the resemblances of the law's problems to the problems of other disciplines in dealing with evidence are perhaps at their maximum. And yet the problems are quite different.

Importance of Rule

It will be noticed in the first place that, while the issue to be decided is formally one of fact only, the rule of law is nevertheless functioning importantly. For it is the rule which makes the fact significant. If, for example, a child could not inherit, the question of the claimant's parentage could be left to his biographer or to the genealogists. This relationship of law and fact becomes even more important when the law is disputed, a situation discussed in Part II below. But the relationship is of more than analytical interest even when the law is undisputed. If the defendant in the murder case is an unpopular member of the community, it may be vital to the law's purposes to be sure that the inquiry is rigorously confined to those matters which bear directly upon the question whether the defendant fired the shot.

Evidence Different

The kinds of evidence used by the law in making determinations of adjudicative fact are unlike those used by other disciplines in pursuance of their objectives.

The adjudicative facts of interest to the law, being historical facts, will rarely be triable by the experimental methods of the natural sciences. To be sure, ballistics tests in the murder case may prove beyond rational dispute that the bullet which killed the victim came from the defendant's gun. Laboratory tests in the breach-of-warranty case may settle beyond question the quality of the goods. And blood tests in the inheritance controversy may show that it is virtually impossible that the claimant was the child of the deceased. But these instances will be exceptional. For the most part the law must settle disputed questions of adjudicative fact by reliance upon the ambiguous implications of non-fungible "traces"—traces on human brains and on pieces of paper and traces in the form of unique arrangements of physical objects.

Furthermore, the law uses different evidence and uses it in a different way than other disciplines do even when those disciplines are similarly interested in the determination of historical facts. These differences result from the fact that what is involved, when the most distinctive practices of the law in the handling of evidence come into play, is the formal and official settlement of a controversy.

Role of Formal Adjudication

To understand the law's peculiar ways of treating evidence it is necessary to have some appreciation of the role which formal adjudication plays in the total functioning of the legal system.

A contested lawsuit is society's last line of defense in the indispensable effort to secure the peaceful settlement of social conflicts. In the overwhelming majority of instances, the general directions of the law function smoothly with no controversy whatever. When controversies do arise, the overwhelming majority of them are settled informally or, if formally, without a contest, as by plea of guilty in a criminal case. In almost all these situations lawyers are likely to handle evidence in the same common-sense fashion that anybody else would, unless special calculations are called for by a real possibility of formal litigation.

When a question has reached the point of a contested trial, however, its whole context is changed. Victory, and not accommodation, is the objective of the parties. The adversary atmosphere and the delays of litigation naturally repel evidence, especially testimony and things under the control of disinterested persons, so that the litigants have available for use only the partisan and coerced residue after people with ingenuity have made themselves anonymous. That residue is culled by the parties with a view not so much to establishing the whole truth as to winning the case. And the evidence which survives this attrition (and the exclusionary rules of evidence described below) is communicated to the trier of fact in an emotion-charged setting.

In judging the law's handling of its task of fact-finding in this setting, it is necessary always to bear in mind that this *is* a last-ditch process in which something more is at stake than the truth only of the specific matter in contest. There is at stake also that confidence of the public generally in the impartiality and fairness of public settlement of disputes which is essential if the ditch is to be held and the settlements accepted peaceably.

Certainty Not Required

The law does not require absolute assurance of the perfect correctness of particular decisions. While it is of course important that the court be right in its determinations of fact, it is also important that the court decide the case when the parties ask for the decision and on the basis of the evidence presented by the parties. A decision must be made now, one way or the other. To require certainty or even near-certainty in such a context would be impracticable and undesirable. The law thus compromises.

The compromise is expressed in the formulas used to guide decision of questions of adjudicative fact. In a criminal case, guilt need not be found beyond all doubt; the trier of the fact must be satisfied of the defendant's guilt only "beyond a reasonable doubt." In a civil case, the facts are ordinarily to be found on the basis of "a preponderance of the evidence"; this phrase is generally defined as meaning simply "more likely than not." The formula for determining whether a case should even be submitted to a jury assumes a wide leeway for differing judgments. The question for the trial judge is whether a "reasonable jury" on the evidence submitted could find that the facts have been proved by a preponderance of the evidence. The judge uses a similar formula in determining whether a verdict already rendered by the jury may stand, and so does the reviewing court in deciding whether to upset either the jury's verdict or the trial judge's own finding if the trial judge sat without a jury.

Meaning of Probability

It may be suggested parenthetically at this point that, while it is clear that the law satisfies itself with less than certainty, it is not clear that the formulas mentioned above always describe correctly the degree of certainty which the law actually requires. Consider the formula that in a civil case the facts must be determined on a more-likely-than-not basis. In the first place, the probabilities are determined in a most subjective and unscientific way: the trier of fact simply asks itself which of the contesting contradictory propositions according to the trier's limited experience more nearly squares with the evidence. In the second place, the law refuses to honor its own formula when the evidence is coldly "statistical." A court would not, for example, hold the government liable to a farmer for injuries inflicted on him by his mule frightened by a "buzzing" jet plane if the only evidence that the pilot was a member of the Air Force (rather than a civilian) was that most of the pilots flying jets that day were Air Force personnel. This would be true even though the farmer could show that as much as 70 or 80 per cent of the jet pilots in the vicinity that day were of the Air Force.

The court, on the other hand, would certainly allow recovery if the evidence was that 100 per cent of the pilots were Air Force personnel, and would probably allow it if all of them were except a negligible few. Similarly, the court might allow recovery if the farmer, instead of introducing the statistical evidence, testified that he got a fleeting glimpse of the pilot's cap and that it was distinctively Air Force headgear. The court somehow feels more comfortable permitting a finding to be based on such eye-witness testimony even though the probative value of such testimony is itself determined ultimately by home-spun "statistics" in the mind of the trier of fact and even though the eye-witness testimony is probably no more indicative of the truth than is the evidence as to the proportion of Air Force pilots in the air.

Even in the case as originally stated—with the farmer producing solely the statistical evidence—the court might allow recovery if the reason for the farmer's dearth of evidence is the irrelevant fact that the government refused without justification to cooperate in the farmer's search for the offending pilot. And, though according to the more-likely-than-not formula it is irrelevant, the court might be swayed in its demand for evidence by the size of the stakes—a more elaborate presentation would naturally be expected if the farmer was claiming $100,000 in damages than if he was claiming $100.

Consistency Not Required

The law does not require that the same adjudicative fact be found the same way in two separate litigations. It is possible, for example, that two passengers injured in the same bus accident may each bring suits against the bus company, both relying on the allegation that the bus driver went through a red light. The law permits the trier of fact in the second case to find that the light was green even though the trier of fact in the first case found that the light was red (indeed, the law will not even permit the second trier of fact to know what the first one held). This willingness to tolerate inconsistency is peculiar to the law. It emphasizes the role of litigation as a mode of settlement of particular disputes, usually between two parties. Persons not participating in the particular adjudication, not having been given their day in court, are not bound by the findings of particular facts.

It should be added, however, that the law usually provides escape for persons "caught in the middle," such as a warehouseman faced with demands for the goods from the bailor and from an outsider claiming that the goods were stolen from him, or such as a store owner sued by a consumer because the manufacturer allegedly included a stone in a can of peas. To avoid the harshness of inconsistent findings of fact in such cases, the law has procedures for bringing all three parties into the same action. But even here the findings of fact are binding only upon the parties to the litigation.

Trial Procedures

The most conspicuous difference between the law's problems in determining historical facts and those of other disciplines lies in the procedure of decision. Other disciplines rely primarily on the method of inquiry, reflection, and report by trained investigators. In other disciplines the final conclusions as to key facts are drawn by experts, and the conclusions may be changed if they are found later—after further inquiry and reflection—to be wrong. The law, in contrast, depends in most formal proceedings upon presentation by the disputants in public hearing before an impartial tribunal, a tribunal previously uninformed about the matters in dispute. And findings of fact by the tribunal are usually final so far as the law is concerned.

Typical of such formal proceedings is the trial in court. A trial suffers from immobility. It suffers from shortage and inflexibility of time. It is dependent largely upon non-expert sources of information and upon non-expert evaluators of information (the jury). In addition, proof at a trial is rather strictly governed by procedural rules called rules of evidence.

What are some of the rules of evidence?

An obvious limitation on proof at a trial—but one which would apply in any rational inquiry—is that the proof must be relevant to a disputed issue. And, of course, the proof should be sufficiently material to be worth the time its presentation consumes. Other limitations on proof at a trial are not so obvious. Much evidence is excluded in spite of its materiality.

"Over-valued" Evidence

Some rules, we might say, are designed to exclude evidence to which the jury might give too much weight:

1. There is a strict (and largely archaic) rule excluding relevant hearsay evidence. Ostensibly this is because second-hand evidence, unsworn to and untested by cross-examination, is unreliable. But actually, conscientious juries are capable of discounting such evidence appropriately. The real reasons for the Hearsay Rule seem to be: (a) it forces the parties to produce better (first-hand) evidence; (b) it gives the court a handy tool for excising time-consuming, but usually relatively useless, testimony; (c) it prevents errant juries from basing an essential finding upon the slender reed of hearsay evidence; and—one must admit— (d) it is, with its sixteen exceptions (more or less), a technicality in which the trial lawyer has an intellectual investment and a valuably exclusive expertise.

2. There is a rule against "opinion" evidence. This rule, which sometimes exasperates laymen, is designed to confine a witness to a description of what he perceived and to reserve the function of inference for the jury. Only an expert qualified to the satisfaction of the court may testify to the inferences he drew from his perceptions, unless of course the matter—like drunkenness or sanity or speed—is something which one can scarcely express (and perhaps not even perceive) in other than conclusory terms.

3. There is a rule against so-called "prejudicial" evidence. Under

this heading the courts may exclude evidence of a criminal defendant's prior convictions or inflammatory photographs or scientific evidence such as lie-detector tests, the reliability of which has not been established.

4. Some witnesses will not be heard by the court because they are "incompetent." In the old days this rule excluded testimony by anyone with an interest in the outcome! Even today most courts, in actions against estates, refuse to hear testimony of survivors as to transactions with the deceased. And potential witnesses may not be heard if they are insane or if they are too young to understand the oath.

Privileges

All the above rules reflect the fear that the evidence will be given too much weight. Another group of rules excludes relevant evidence on the theory that the value of the evidence to the court is not great enough to overcome some other social value served by suppressing the evidence. These are the "privileges." The government need not reveal its military secrets, nor even its official secrets nor the names of its secret informers—though, of course, in a criminal prosecution the government may have to elect either to divulge its secrets to the defendant or to drop the prosecution. A wife cannot be compelled in a criminal case to testify against her husband and in any case she may not be required to divulge things he told her in confidence. A similar privilege applies to communications by a client to his attorney and in some jurisdictions to communications by a penitent to his priest, by a patient to his doctor, by a client to his accountant, and by a person to a social worker. Some statutes give newspaper reporters the privilege of refusing to divulge their sources of information. Well-known is the privilege against self-incrimination. It is justified partly by the fact that it tends to induce law-enforcement officials not to use the rubber hose and red pepper, partly by the fact that it spares squeamish modern man the unpleasantness of seeing a fellow mortal put squarely between self-destruction and perjury, and partly by the fact that, by limiting the government to evidence outside our own heads, the privilege makes it appropriately difficult for the government to punish you and me for beliefs we hold or for infractions of insufficient notoriety to be of real concern to society.

Closely related to the privileges is the rule now becoming applicable in most courts that evidence will not be received if it was obtained by illegal means—that is, evidence obtained by illegal search and seizure, by wire-tapping, or by coercion or inducements or even during prolonged detention of a defendant. This rule is perhaps to be understood mainly as a manifestation of the courts' unwillingness to be in effect accessories after the fact to illegal police methods. But it is often justified also as a deterrent to such methods by making them unprofitable.

There are other rules which we will only mention: rules governing the presumptions which apply when there is no evidence on a point; the allocation of the fact-finding function between the judge and the jury; the extent to which the judge or jury may use information not offered in evidence; the order in which parties proceed, and the order in which witnesses are examined; the manner and scope of such examinations; the limits of impeachment and support of witnesses; the manner in which the court's attention is called to errors; and the function of the judge in ruling on alleged errors.

"Bent" Facts

One more characteristic of legal fact-finding needs to be noted—one which enjoys clandestine respectability in the law but which in other disciplines is a hallmark of intellectual dishonesty: the facts are sometimes "bent" to serve an ulterior purpose. It is important to proper administration of the law that the public believe in the humanity and justice of decisions. This value the law seeks to serve partly through the institution of the jury trial. The jury, representing "the people," is deliberately inserted as a kind of cushion between the individual on the one hand and the coercive power of the state on the other. The jury, always in criminal cases, and within broad limits in civil cases, is allowed to thwart the law's commands—in effect to find the facts untruthfully—if it is not satisfied with the justness of the commands as applied to the case in hand.

*   *   *

No doubt the method of formal presentation of evidence before an impartial but uninformed tribunal, subject to the rules which such a presentation seems to require, will not always prove to be the best method of ascertaining the truth about past happenings. The law makes no assumption that it will. It deliberately sacrifices some aids to the ascertainment of truth which might be useful in particular cases in order, partly, to satisfy the practical exigencies of the need for an immediate and definite decision and in order, partly, to serve what are deemed to be more nearly ultimate social values. It is an important question whether these sacrifices are justified—whether, granting the possibilities of improvement in peripheral matters of detail, the main outlines of the law's approach to the task of determining questions of this kind are not entitled to general acceptance.

II. THE APPLICATION OF UNCERTAIN OR DISPUTED LAW TO DISPUTED FACTS

We turn now to a different type of situation in which both the law and the facts are in issue. Just as a court must decide disputed questions of fact one way or another when a case is presented to it for decision, so also must it decide all relevant questions of law. Sometimes doubt about the law can be readily resolved. If the resolution yields a ground of decision in the form of a technical rule, as earlier defined, then the remaining problems of decision will be those already described in Part I. But the matter is frequently not as simple as this.

It will help to illuminate some of the difficulties to inquire why it so often happens that the law *is* uncertain or disputed.

Laws Deliberately Vague

Lay opinion is likely to expect the law to be largely in the form of technical rules, leaving nothing to be decided in the application but the happening or non-happening of the events which bring the rule into play. But reflection will show that a near-miracle occurs whenever the law is successfully stated in this way. For this means that all of the indefinite number of situations governed by the rule have been accurately foreseen in all their relevant dimensions, that the requirements of public policy with respect to them have been fully and acceptably determined, and that the determinations have been accurately communicated from the past to the present.

But human experience is infinitely variable, and the law must deal with most of its manifestations. Accurately to foresee all these manifestations within even a narrow category of experience—assuming that the type of experience can be categorized at all—is commonly impossible. To make in advance an acceptable determination of what public policy requires even in the situations which can be foreseen will often be either impossible or unwise. And the effort to express in unambiguous language such determinations as can be made is beset with traps.

So it happens that the law is replete with devices for the postponement of some or even most of the elements of decision until from the perspective of application the decision can be more accurately or wisely made. Often the postponement takes the form of an avowed delegation of discretion of one type or another, as to a legislature in deciding what statutes to enact, to an administrative agency in deciding what regulations to promulgate, or to private persons in deciding what contracts or wills to make or what associations to form, and the like. But the postponement may also take the form of a direction which purports to govern the substance of the decisions which are ultimately to be made but which is nevertheless in some respects deliberately indeterminate in its content. In carrying out such a direction, a tribunal of authoritative application has a double job to do: besides resolving the questions of historical or adjudicative fact which in the end are seen to be relevant, it must settle, or in some fashion deal with, the postponed questions of policy.

The Legal "Standard"

A simple example of postponement by the device of indeterminate language is the use in the governing direction of a *standard*. Such a standard may be expressed in terms of ordinary human experiences. For example: "Use due care in driving an automobile"—due care being the standard, and due care meaning such care as a prudent person would use in the circumstances to avoid injury to others. Or it may call for a highly specialized evaluation of behavior and its consequences. For example: "Do not make any contract, combination, or conspiracy which unreasonably restrains trade or commerce among the several states."

Notice the distinguishing characteristic of this type of indeterminate law: the direction requires in its application a qualitative comparison with general experience of the particular instance or instances of experience which are in issue. The trier of fact in such cases has to decide not only what actually happened in the particular case but what generally happens and ought to happen in other such cases, and to compare the two.

In the course of application of such an indeterminate law in one or more cases, a much more determinate law—call it a technical rule—

may emerge. For example: "It is unlawful (that is, lacking in due care) to attempt to pass another car when vision over the distance necessary to accomplish the passing is obscured"; or, "It is unlawful (that is, an unreasonable restraint of trade or commerce) for two or more sellers of the same commodity to agree to charge the same price." Such a rule may not emerge, however, so that the law is left in the more vague and flexible form of the standard, requiring in each case an *ad hoc* judgment by the trier of fact.

Two things are especially to be observed in the two illustrations that have been given. The first has to do with the interrelationship between facts and law, and the other with the kinds of facts involved.

Chicken-and-Egg Relationship

Consider the fact-law relationship in the automobile illustration. Notice that it is only when it is deemed wrongful to pass with one's vision obscured that we need to inquire whether the defendant did it; but at the same time it is only when the evidence permits the conclusion that the defendant did try to pass with his vision obscured that the legal question whether this is wrongful is presented. Here we have, in perhaps too elementary a form to seem meaningful, a cardinal aspect of the way in which the law works and grows. The issues of fact arise out of the law but, at the point of application of law, the issues of law also arise out of the facts. This chicken-and-egg relationship exists in any case in which indeterminacy in the law must be resolved; and such cases are innumerable. The difficulty obviously is acute when both law and facts are uncertain and in dispute. The difficulty in this acute form is especially worth calling to the attention of an audience of non-lawyers because it lies at the heart of the trouble which lawyers and specialists in other disciplines continually have wnen they try to work together, particularly in the preparation and trial of litigated cases.

The lawyer working with an economist in an antitrust proceeding, for example, has to determine what matters of economic fact the existing formulations of legal doctrine make relevant, as well as how these matters are to be prcved. If the law is unsettled and growing and the problem has novel elements, he must also consider what matters of economic fact a court or administrative agency may judge to be relevant. Such a decision calls for legal training. The court or agency does not have a completely free hand in the resolution of indeterminacies in the applicable law; it must relate its decision in reasoned fashion to principles and policies already settled and to analogous applications of these principles and policies. A trained lawyer will have a sense of what leeway exists. These and other considerations suggest that the lawyer should be in command of strategic planning in preparing the prosecution or defense of such a case, and tell the economist what is and is not worth-while to look for.

But this plainly will not do—at least not without material qualification. For the economist is the expert in observing economic behavior and appraising economic effects, and he must have some degree of freedom in making his observations and appraisal. Again and again he will notice economic phenomena which the lawyer would miss but which, when called to the lawyer's attention, will seem to alter the character of the legal problem. So the truth is that neither can be in complete command. They have to learn how to work together, each aware of the indispensability of the other, and each having a sense of the other's potential contribution in developing the analysis.

"Legislative" Facts

The other aspect of the two illustrations earlier given which deserves notice is the special character of the facts bearing on the question whether passing with vision obscured should be declared to constitute, without more, a failure of due care, or on the question whether an agreement between competitors to fix prices should be held to be *per se* an unreasonable restraint of trade.

The facts which guide judgment about whether an indeterminate standard should be particularized in the form of a technical rule for certain classes of cases—such as a rule proscribing passing with vision obscured, or price-fixing—are not facts about a particular event which bear upon the question whether that event should be subsumed under, or brings into play, a general direction or law. Rather they are facts which bear upon the question whether a general proposition of law should be formulated in one way or another. They concern not particular happenings but general behavior and the general tendencies, consequences, and evaluation of behavior. They are "legislative," as distinguished from adjudicative, facts. They are facts, correspondingly, which are of concern to many who are not parties to the litigation and which ought not to be left to be settled solely under the aegis of the adversaries before the court.

Legislatures, of course, consider facts of this kind in deciding whether to enact a statute. So do courts in formulating grounds of decision. There are differences, however: *first*, the court is concerned with such facts only to the extent necessary to formulate a just ground for the decision of the controversy before it, and, *second*, the court is under the necessity of relating the ground of decision which it formulates in some rational fashion to the underlying direction which it is elaborating, and hence is specially concerned with facts which help it to do this.

Here, in the judicial (or quasi-judicial, administrative) ascertainment of "legislative" facts, we have a whole new range of questions of evidence and inference in the law. For the most part the traditional rules of evidence discussed in Part I above either do not apply at all or apply in distinctive fashion. What rules, then, do apply? What techniques does the law follow?

Limits of time and space prevent a full answer to these questions. But more than these prevent it. For the truth is that these are among the most neglected questions of legal scholarship. An answer undertaken without limit of time or space would at best be argumentative when it was done. An abbreviated summary given to non-lawyers would be open to challenge by other lawyers as either misleading or simply mistaken. Accordingly, only a few tentative suggestions will be ventured.

At the root of the superficially strange neglect of problems of how legislative facts are to be determined by a court is the traditional reluctance of the courts to admit that they are making law at all. Yet make law they do, although it is interstitial, elaborative, law, made or supposed to be made under the discipline of an effort to show or be able to show a reasoned connection between the newly made law and established doctrines of law which underlie and justify it. In the making of this law the courts have constant need of knowledge to inform and guide their judgment.

Sources of Knowledge

The need for knowledge is occasionally met by expert testimony. Thus, if the question is whether industrial common stocks should be declared to be a proper investment for a trustee, economists and financial advisers can be called to testify to investment experience with such stocks. If the question is whether the so-called *Durham* rule recently announced by the Court of Appeals for the District of

Columbia should be substituted for the traditional *M'Naghten* rules in determining the availability of the defense of insanity in a criminal case, the testimony of doctors and of psychiatrists and psychologists can throw such light as contemporary knowledge in these fields is able to throw upon the court's problem. Receipt of testimony of this kind is by no means uncommon, although the difference between expert testimony offered to prove the happening or non-happening of an historical event and expert testimony offered to guide the court in its elaboration of law is not always noted. But the puzzle is why lawyers do not offer, nor courts invite, such testimony more often. Part of the explanation, no doubt, is a lack of a sense of competence in dealing with it.

Another accepted way of providing the court with knowledge about relevant legislative facts is by quotation and citation, in briefs and argument of counsel, of publications in the field, or by independent research in such publications on the part of the judge or his law clerk. Thus, in the *Durham* case the court relied heavily on writings of lawyers and psychiatrists on the problem of legal insanity —writings which apparently came to its attention in both ways. The absolute number of judicial opinions which contain references to non-legal studies of social and economic facts in support of legal conclusions is very considerable. But relatively speaking such opinions are exceptional. Here again diffidence in dealing with an unfamiliar kind of material, particularly when it is in any substantial degree controversial, undoubtedly plays a part. But the problem is a real one. How *are* the courts to safeguard themselves from being misled, and the losing party from being surprised and justifiably resentful, when the judges venture into areas in which they are necessarily inexpert? The wonder, and the regret, is only that so few judicial opinions or discussions by legal scholars have come to grips with the difficulties and begun to make headway in solving them.

Enthusiasts for judicial reform from time to time have suggested the desirability of equipping the courts with research staffs of their own, of the type which help administrative agencies in acquiring social and economic information. But virtually nothing has come of these proposals, or of other plans for turning a court into a kind of subsidiary legislature. For guidance in the elaboration of legal doctrine, the courts continue to rely largely on general knowledge with modest help, primarily in noncontroversial areas, from expert testimony and research in existing publications.

Time, expense, and professional habituations furnish a large part of the explanation for this dependence upon what most people know without looking into books, or upon established and generally accepted book learning. But there may be a subtler explanation also. Courts are engaged largely in adjudication after the event, usually between two parties. The courts must therefore always be alert to the dangers of announcing law which is essentially *ex post facto* as to the parties and which is *in absentia* as to persons who will in later litigation encounter the new law. A ground of decision which can be justified only by judicial resolution of the disputes of experts in other disciplines, or which depends primarily upon data freshly collected through a judicially supervised research project framed with an eye to the particular case, is not likely to seem to the parties to be fairly within the range of their reasonable expectations at the time they acted or to later litigants to have been determined with adequate regard to their interests. It is not likely, in other words, to seem just.

III. THE FRAMING OF A LEGISLATIVE ENACTMENT

A legislature, unlike a court, is free from the necessity of relating its determinations, by some process of reasoning, to principles and policies or standards already settled in the law. Within the broad limits set by constitutional restraints, it can make a new social policy, if this seems to be the wise thing to do; and, if necessary, it can create new institutional structures to carry out the policy. This it can do with full representation and full opportunity for hearing of all the interests affected. The new policy, moreover, can usually be made to operate prospectively, free from the opprobrium which attaches to retrospective law-making. Here then, it might seem, is the point of decision at which not only scientific investigation but scientific determination could be most profitably employed in the law.

The short answer to this suggestion, in a paper dealing with the ways in which the law actually handles evidence, is that the methods of decision and, for the most part, even the methods of inquiry in fact used by legislatures are not "scientific"—in the sense at least in which that word is used in the natural sciences and in the behavioral sciences. The questions worth discussing are why this is so, and what the possibilities are for the development in the future of a science of legislation which is more nearly "scientific."

Piecemeal Relevancy of Data

Legislatures, of course, receive a vast amount of information and opinion relevant to the subject matter of pending bills, and occasionally this may be presented in the form of a study or report which would pass muster with reputable scholars in the branch of knowledge involved. Indeed, such material finds its way into transcripts of committee hearings and legislative debates much more readily than it does into judicial opinions. Moreover, the findings and opinions of experts are given some weight (sometimes even too much), the weight usually varying according to the degree of acceptance which the conclusions appear to command among other experts in the field, and varying also according to the sometimes inscrutable differences in the prestige which different disciplines enjoy with the public. The march of knowledge, in other words, has an impact on legislatures just as it does on courts and for that matter on businessmen or labor leaders.

Information and opinion of the kind just described, however, deal characteristically with only one facet of the total problem before the legislature, although the facet may be important and in the end even decisive. For example, the evidence submitted to the legislature may show that an existing law is not working the way it was supposed to work, or that a newly developing problem has a magnitude not theretofore appreciated. Or the evidence may tend to establish or refute some other element of the whole case in support of a proposed enactment. But reliance on such piecemeal information is a far cry from the working use of techniques of data-collection and analysis to yield firm conclusions in the form of the proposition that "This proposed bill, drafted as it now is, should (or should not) be enacted," or that "This statute should (or should not) be amended in this way," or that "This statute should (or should not) be repealed."

Importance of Politics and Policy

Part of the reason why there is no working use of techniques of this more comprehensive kind is, of course, that the legislature is a political body made up of representatives of constituents whose desires do not yield readily to unpalatable findings of experts, or to logic. But that is only part of the reason.

The truth is that, in relation to problems of any complexity, data about past and present social experience can usually carry even a legislator with the most single-minded devotion to the public interest only a short distance on the way to his final vote.

This fact is perhaps most clearly demonstrated by observing how disinterested experts proceed in drawing model statutes such as the Uniform Commercial Code or the American Law Institute's projected Model Penal Code. The process is not one of the laborious collection of data, followed by the drawing of rational inferences from the data. This does not mean that the teachings of non-legal disciplines are ignored. On the contrary, generally accepted teachings are respected, and the opinions of experts in doubtful matters are sought out. But these teachings and opinions help to frame the problems more accurately rather than to solve them. The actual process of arriving at an agreement upon a final draft is one of interchange of argument and opinion and of the continuous subjection of alternative formulations to the raking fire of competent criticism until at last a formulation is found which appears to survive the test as well as may be. The process, in other words, is one which is adapted to the solution of problems which are essentially problems of policy and which do not respond, therefore, to any test of objective fact, but only to the test of informed judgment.

Paucity of Useful Data

A simple, practical reason why legislators, or committees of drafting experts, are forced to proceed in this fashion is that there is not ordinarily available any substantial body of either legal or non-legal learning which is pointed directly to the solution of the concrete problem with which they have to deal. Existing non-legal studies, if they are available at all, prove almost invariably to be frustratingly diffuse, even when they are aimed in a general way at the problem with which the legislature has to deal. Take, for example, the abundant literature of psychological and psychiatric criticism of the traditional legal tests of insanity as a defense in a criminal prosecution. When the draftsmen of the Model Penal Code sought to extract from this literature some constructive ideas for the formulation of a better test, they were able to get from it little more than an expression of dissatisfaction with the existing law. This dissatisfaction and some of the reasons given for it were persuasive of the need for a revision of the traditional tests. But *the particular form* which the revision took owed relatively little to psychological and psychiatric opinion and virtually nothing, directly, to psychological and psychiatric data.

If existing studies of past and present social experience prove inadequate as a guide for the framing of a law for the control of future experience, there is, of course, always the possibility of seeking illumination by having a special study made which is aimed at the draftsmen's specific problem. Fortunately there is usually time for the preparation of such a study, since a legislature, unlike a court, does not have to act right away. But relatively few such studies are attempted at all, and fewer still prove to be of any substantial value. One reason for this is that the accumulation of reliable data about past and present social experience even in seemingly minor areas of inquiry is time-consuming and appallingly expensive. But a more important reason is that the problems of deciding just what data to collect and how to interpret them after they have been collected are extraordinarily difficult and often unsuspectedly treacherous. For the effects of any given law or social practice under investigation can seldom be isolated from the effects of other related laws and social practices. How then is it to be decided what effects are to be investigated and to what causes they are to be attributed?

The Enigma of the Future

These difficulties are multiplied whenever an effort is made to deduce from past and present experience a prediction about future experience. There is wisdom, it is ventured, in the legislator's instinctive wariness of such predictions. For he is being asked to move from uncertainty to uncertainty squared, and often squared again.

A simple illustration will make the point in an elementary form. More or less "scientific" investigations have seemed to demonstrate again and again that severe criminal penalties are ineffectual in securing compliance with a law which a substantial segment of the populace does not wish to obey. But studies of the behavior of conquered peoples during the period of Nazi occupation seem to show that the threat of the death penalty was highly effective in securing compliance with hated laws so long as the penalty was rigorously enforced. It was only when the relaxation of enforcement effort, induced by preoccupation with other problems, resulted in a good gambling chance of violating the law with impunity that enforcement broke down despite the penalty. The moral suggested for free societies, of course, is that severe penalties fail, not because they are inherently ineffectual, but only for lack of adequate machinery to enforce them consistently and of an adequately ruthless disposition to make use of the machinery. The illustration may be thought to show the value of sufficiently perceptive studies of how people behave in response to legal commands, as indeed it does. But it also suggests that there are endless variables affecting behavior which an investigator of social phenomena is in continual danger of overlooking and which stir doubts in interpretation even when they have not been overlooked.

It seems that in general no report of past and present social behavior, however suggestive it may be, can afford proof to a doubting legislator concerning the future operation of a law. Still less can it be expected to prove that any particular proposed law will work better than any alternative. For the choices which a legislature makes for the future are choices among a virtual infinity of possibilities. It is not feasible to have experimental runs even of the leading possibilities. To rely on past experience, instead of a trial run, is to encounter always the difficulty not only of the incompleteness of the experience but of its inconclusiveness. The experience is necessarily inconclusive because behavior is always a function of its context. The context of social living is always changing. Indeed, the statute under consideration may itself contemplate major changes in the context. How people will respond to these changes cannot be determined by data. At best it can only be estimated by an exercise of judgment which is informed not only by data but by human wisdom and by the insight, in particular, that human beings are stubbornly resistant to change, and especially manipulated change, and endlessly resourceful in their devices for defeating it.

Disputed Objectives

The difficulties which have been mentioned exist even when relevant data about past behavior are available, and even when there is substantial agreement about the human and social responses which it is desired to bring about in the future. As has been seen, the first condition is not usually satisfied. And when important measures are under consideration, the second condition almost never is. Thus, controversy about how it would be desirable to have people respond to the proposed enactment is added to controversy about how they are likely to respond. Nor, ordinarily, are the two types of uncertainties sharply differentiated. What characteristically will be in issue will be a complex calculation of social gains and losses, with all or most of the factors in the equation in debate. Is the questioned likelihood of achieving these questionably desirable ends worth these costs of both questioned probability and questioned undesirability? It will generally be conceded that the ends which people ought to seek in society lend themselves even less readily to determination by the method of inference from objectively established data than do the results which a given law is likely to bring about.

So it is that questions about the enactment of proposed bills must be decided by the exercise of judgment—by judgment based as much as possible on experience and reflection, but by judgment nevertheless. To anyone who is skeptical of this conclusion a challenge can be given: name a single statute, either enacted or proposed, which has ever been demonstrated, by methods which would be approved in the experimental sciences, to be "right" in the sense of being better adapted to its purpose than any alternative kind of legislation, let alone naming a statute whose purpose has been demonstrated by such methods to be "right."

A *"Science" of Legislation*

There is room—indeed, there is a great need—for a science of legislation which is a science in the sense that it seeks to make explicit its assumptions about the nature of the problems of man in society and the basis for assumptions, and then tries to organize and expand knowledge about how to solve the problems, while holding itself in readiness to revise the underlying assumptions as the expansion of knowledge may require.

Such a science, it is ventured, must build primarily upon the systematic study of the various institutional processes, both official and private, by which the problems of social living can be and are settled, and upon reflection about what is necessary to make these processes work more satisfactorily. No society can exist, so far as we know, without regularized procedures for deciding questions of concern both to the society as a whole and to individuals as members of the society. Study of the questions to be decided and of the decisions which ought to be made must therefore begin with study of the procedures which are the inescapable context of decision; and a quest for improvement in the quality of the decisions has to begin with effort to improve the quality of the procedures.

It will be apparent that the quality of procedures for the decision of questions which rest unavoidably upon the exercise of judgment cannot be improved by turning over the responsibility for decision to experts in sociological research, or by encouraging either private or official rubber-stamping of the "findings" of such experts. For the workability of decisions of this kind, when they involve telling people how to behave in matters which are of consequence to them, depends in large part upon their acceptability. In other societies, the authority of a monarch or the prestige of a ruling class has often sufficed to secure the general acceptance of prudential judgments about how the citizenry should conduct themselves. But in today's world none of the sciences of society has yet succeeded in securing for its exponents a comparable authority or prestige. Judicial decisions about how people should behave command acceptance, when they do command it, both because of public confidence in the disinterestedness of the tribunal and because the decisions are thought to depend not upon a prudential judgment but upon a process of reasoning from authoritatively settled premises. When these conditions cannot be satisfied, experience seems to show that acceptability depends upon the maximum feasible participation in making the decision by those who will be affected by it.

In this view the method of free negotiation among interested individuals or groups in a reasonably equal negotiating position will be seen to be a "scientific" method for the private settlement of prudential questions about future behavior, in the sense of being well-adapted to its purpose. In relation to questions of this kind which need to be settled by the highest official authority in the society, the method of controlled negotiation through the procedures of legislative deliberation and decision will be seen to be similarly "scientific." In both contexts of decision, there is need for making better use of existing knowledge in all branches of the science of society as well as of the trained sense of experts in matters as to which no definite knowledge can be said to exist. A better use does not consist, however, merely in displacing the judgment of contracting parties and legislators, but in informing their judgment so that they will be able to make wiser estimates of future human behavior and long-run human wants.

One may guess that a future science of legislation will proceed upon the observation that human abilities are ultimately the most important of social resources for the satisfaction of human needs and wants, and upon the further observation that the environment which is most favorable to the development of these abilities, as well as to the fulfilling of these satisfactions, is one which provides the maximum opportunity and encourages the maximum growth of individual capacity to make effectual and responsible decisions concerning the direction of human and social life. And one may hope that the investigations of many kinds of social scientists will help in confirming these hypotheses.

If these surmises and hopes are sound, the conclusions of the third part of this paper will not appear to be a matter for regret. For if, indeed, the exercise of responsible judgment in the direction of human and social life is of the essence of the whole social enterprise of realizing the potentialities of human existence, then the idea that it would be a good thing if expertly assembled data *could* be made to displace judgment is at war with the very purpose and the principal *modus operandi* of a free society.

The Nature of Clinical Evidence

ERIK H. ERIKSON

I

THE LETTER of invitation to contribute to this Colloquium puts into the center of my assignment the question *"How does a . . . clinician really work?"* and gives to this task the necessary latitude by inquiring about the clinician's reliance on *intuition* ("or some other version of personal judgment") and about the use of *objectified tests,* ("relatively uniform among clinicians of different theoretical persuasions"). The letter concludes: "To the extent that intuition plays a role, in what way does the clinician seek to discipline its operation: by his conceptual framework? by long personal experience?" This emphasizes, within the inquiry of how a clinician works, the question of how he thinks.

Such an invitation is a hospitable one, encouraging the guest, as it were, to come as he is. It spares the clinician whatever temptation he might otherwise feel to claim inclusion in the social register of long established sciences by demonstrating that he, too, can behave the way they do. He can state from the outset that in one essay he can hardly offer more than phenomenological groundwork, perhaps necessarily of a markedly personal nature.

The invitation, in my case, is addressed to a psychotherapist of a particular "persuasion": my training is that of a Freudian psychoanalyst, and I train others—in the vast majority physicians—in this method. I shall make a sincere attempt to place vocation over persuasion and to formulate how the nature of clinical evidence is determined by a clinician's daily task. If I, nevertheless, seem to feel beholden to Freud's conceptual system—that is, a system originated around the turn of this century by a physician schooled in physicalist physiology—the reason is not narrowly partisan: few will deny that from such transfer of physicalistic concepts to psychology new modes of clinical thinking have developed in our time.

"Clinical," of course, is an old word. In the days when the church was the primary guardian of man's well-being, clinical referred to a priest's administrations at the deathbed—then the only gateway to true health, since all through life man owed a death. Later, the word was primarily applied to medical ministrations, as science and humanism joined forces in taking the short-range point of view that man owes himself a long and healthy life, or at any rate one free from disease. In our time and in the Western world, the word clinical is expanding rapidly to include not only medical but also social considerations, not only physical well-being but also mental health, not only matters of cure but also of prevention, not only therapy but also research. This means that clinical work is now allied with many brands of evidence and overlaps with many methodologies. Yet, I feel called upon to speak of the nature of evidence gathered in the individual clinical encounter itself.

Let me briefly review the elements making up the clinical core of medical work in general as the encounter of two people, one in need of help, the other in the possession of professional methods. Their *contract* is a therapeutic one: in exchange for a fee, and for information revealed in confidence, the physician promises to act for the benefit of the individual patient, within the ethos of the profession. There usually is a *complaint*, consisting of the description of more or less circumscribed pain or dysfunction, and there are *symptoms*, visible or otherwise localizable. There follows an attempt at an *anamnesis*, an etiological reconstruction of the disturbance, and an *examination*, carried out by means of the physician's naked senses or supported by instruments, which may include the laboratory methods. In evaluating the evidence and in arriving at diagnostic and prognostic inferences (which are really the clinical form of a *prediction*), the physician *thinks clinically*—that is, he scans in his mind different *models* in which different modes of knowledge have found condensation: the *anatomical* structure of the body, the *physiological* functioning of body parts, or the *pathological* processes underlying classified disease entities. A clinical prediction takes its clues from the complaint, the symptoms, and the anamnesis, and makes inferences based on a rapid and mostly preconscious cross-checking against each other of anatomical, physiological and pathological models. On this basis, a *preferred method of treatment* is selected. This is the simplest clinical encounter. In it the patient lends parts of himself to a laboratory procedure and as far as he possibly can, ceases to be a person, i.e., a creature which is more than the sum of its organs.

Any good doctor knows, however, that the patient's complaint is more extensive than his symptom, and the state of sickness more comprehensive than localized pain or dysfunction. As an old Jew put it (and old Jews have a way of speaking for the victims of all nations): "Doctor, my bowels are sluggish, my feet hurt, my heart jumps—and you know, Doctor, I myself don't feel so well either." The treatment, thus, is not limited to local adjustments; it must, and in the case of a "good" doctor automatically does, include a wider view of the complaint, and entail corresponding *interpretations* of the symptom to the patient, often making the "patient himself" an assistant observer and associate doctor. This is especially important, as subsequent appointments become part of a *developing case-history*, which step for step verifies or contradicts whatever predictions had been made and put to test earlier.

This, then, for better or for worse, is the traditional core of the clinical encounter, whether it deals with physical or with mental complaints. But in the special case of the *psychotherapeutic encounter*, a specimen of which I intend to present and to analyze presently, three items crowd out all the others, namely, *complaint, anamnesis*, and *interpretation*. What goes on in the therapist's mind between the verbal complaint addressed to him and the verbal interpretation given in return—this, I take it, is the question to be examined here. But this means: in what way can the psychological clinician make his own perception and thought reliable in the face of the patient's purely verbal and social expression, and in the absence of nonverbal supportive instruments? At this point I am no longer quite so sure that the invitation to "tell us how a . . . clinician really works" was very friendly, after all. For you must suspect that the psychotherapist, in many ways, uses the setting and the terminology of a medical and even a laboratory approach, claiming recourse to an anatomy, a physiology, and a pathology of the mind, without matching the traditional textbook clarity of medical science in any way. To put it briefly, the element of subjectivity, both in the patient's complaints and in the therapist's interpretations, may be vastly greater than in a strictly medical encounter, although this element is in principle not absent from any clinical approach.

Indeed, there is no choice but to put subjectivity into the center of an inquiry into evidence and inference in clinical work. The psychotherapist shares with any clinician the Hippocratic fact that hour by hour he must fulfill a *contract* with individuals who offer themselves to cure and study and who surrender much of their most personal inviolacy in exchange for the expectation that they will emerge from the encounter more whole and less fragmented than when they entered it. The psychotherapist shares with all clinicians the further requirement that even while facing most intimate and emotional matters, he must maintain a constant inner traffic between his often dramatic observations and his conceptual models, however crude they may be. But more than any other clinician the psycho-therapist must include in his field of observation a *specific self-awareness* in the very act of perceiving his patient's actions and reactions. I shall therefore not dwell on the various ways and means, widely invented and refined in our day, of objectifying the clinician's subjectivity through the introduction of essentially non-clinical checks into the clinical procedure. Rather, I shall claim that there is a core of *disciplined subjectivity* in clinical work which it is neither de-sirable nor possible altogether to replace with seemingly more objective methods—methods which originate, as it were, in the machine-tooling of other kinds of work.

II

As I proceed with the task of describing how the clinical method in psychotherapy "actually works," I find that I tentatively place myself next to the historian, although with no intention of crowding him. The words "history taking" and "case history" as used in the clinical field are more than mere figures of speech. They may serve us as a first step in making objective that element of subjectivity which in essence characterizes all the clinical arts and sciences.

R. G. Collingwood defines as an historical process one "in which the past, so far as it is historically known, survives in the present." Thus being "itself a process of thought . . . it exists only in so far as the minds which are parts of it know themselves for parts of it." And again: "History is the life of mind itself which is not mind except so far as it *both lives in historical process and knows itself as so living.*"*

It is not my task to argue the philosophy of history. The analogy between the clinician and the historian as defined by Collingwood to me centers in the case-historian's highly "self-conscious" function in the act of history-taking, and thus in the process of the case. Beyond this the analogy breaks down; it could remain relevant for

---

* R. G. Collingwood, *The Idea of History* (New York: Oxford University Press, 1956), pp. 226-227.

our work only if the historian were also a kind of clinical statesman, correcting events as he records them, and recording as he directs. Such a conscious clinician-historian-statesman may well emerge generations hence from our joint work, although by then he may not use our terms or be aware of our dilemmas. Some of you may already see him seeking a foothold in such crises as economic "recessions," as he alternately interprets what he observes as cyclic, pathological or beneficial, and makes history as he thus interprets it.

Let me restate the psychotherapeutic encounter, then, as an historical one. A person has declared an emergency and has surrendered his self-regulation to a treatment procedure. Besides having become a subjective *patient*, he has accepted the role of a formal *client*. To some degree, he has had to interrupt his autonomous life-history as lived in the unself-conscious balances of his private and his public life in order, for a while, to "favor" a part-aspect of himself and to observe it with the diagnostic help of a curative method: as he is "under observation," he becomes self-observant. As a patient he is inclined, and as a client encouraged, to historicize his own position by thinking back to the onset of the disturbance, and to ponder what world order (magic, scientific, ethical) was violated and must be restored before his "normal" place in history can be reassumed. He participates in becoming a *case*, a fact which he may live down socially, but which, nevertheless, may forever change his own opinion of himself.

The clinician, in turn, appointed to judge the bit of interrupted life put before him, and to introduce himself and his method into it, finds himself part of another man's most intimate life history. Luckily he also remains the functionary of a healing profession with a systematic orientation, based on a coherent world image—be it the theory that man is surrounded by evil spirits, or under the temptation of the devil, or the victim of chemical poisons, or subject to inner conflicts, or the representative of destructive social forces. But in inviting his client to look at himself with the help of professional theories and techniques the clinician makes himself part of the client's life history, even as he asks the client to become a case history in the annals of healing.

In northern California I knew an old Shaman woman who laughed merrily at my conception of mental disease, and then sincerely—to the point of ceremonial tears—told me of her way of sucking the "pains" out of her patients. She was as convinced of her ability to cure and to understand as I was of mine. While occupying extreme opposites in the history of American psychiatry, we felt like colleagues. This feeling was based on some joint sense of the historical relativity of all psychotherapy: the relativity of the patient's outlook on his symptoms; of the role he assumes by dint of being a patient; of the kind of help which he seeks; and of the kinds of help he finds available. The old Shaman woman and I disagreed about the locus of emotional sickness, what it was, and what specific methods would cure it. Yet, when she related the origin of a child's illness to the familial tensions existing within her tribe, when she attributed the "pain" (which had gotten "under a child's skin") to his grandmother's sorcery (ambivalence) I knew she dealt with the same forces, and with the same kinds of conviction, as I did in my part of American culture and in my professional nook. This experience has been repeated in discussions with colleagues who, although not necessarily more "primitive," are oriented toward different psychiatric "persuasions."

To summarize: the disciplined psychotherapist today finds himself heir to medical methods and concepts, and allied with the procedures of the biological sciences. On the other hand, he recognizes his activities as a function of historical processes, and is forced to conclude that in some sense he is "making history" as he "takes" it.

III

It is in such apparent quicksand that we must seek the tracks of clinical evidence. No wonder that often the only clinical material which impresses some as being at all "scientific" is the evidence of the auxiliary methods of psychotherapy—neurological examination, chemical analysis, sociological study, psychological experiment, etc.— all of which derive their laws of evidence from a non-clinical field, and each of which, strictly speaking, puts the patient into nontherapeutic conditions of observation. Each of these methods may "objectify" *some* matters immensely, provide inestimable supportive evidence for *some* theories, and lead to independent methods of cure in *some* classes of patients. But it is not of the nature of the evidence provided in the psychotherapeutic encounter itself.

To introduce such evidence, I need a specimen. This will consist of my reporting to you what a patient *said* to me, how he *behaved* in doing so and what I, in turn, *thought* and *did*—a highly suspect method. And, indeed, we may well stand at the beginning of a period when consultation rooms (already airier and lighter than Freud's) will have, as it were, many more doors open in the direction of an enlightened community's resources, even as they now have research windows in the form of one-way screens, cameras, and recording equipment. For the kind of evidence to be highlighted here, however, it is still essential that, for longer periods or for shorter ones, these doors be closed, soundproof, and impenetrable.

I am not trying to ward off legitimate study of the setting from which our examples come. I know only too well that many of our interpretations seem to be of the variety of that given by one Jew to another in a Polish railroad station. "Where are you going?" asked the first. "To Minsk," said the other. "To Minsk!" exclaimed the first. "You say you go to Minsk so that I should believe you go to Pinsk! You are going to Minsk anyway—so why do you lie?" There is a widespread prejudice that the psychotherapist, point for point, uncovers what he claims the patient "really," and often unconsciously, had in mind, and that he has sufficient Pinsk-Minsk reversals in his technical arsenal to come out with the flat assertion that the evidence is on the side of his claim. It is for this very reason that I will try to demonstrate what method there may be in clinical judgment. I will select as my specimen the most subjective of all data, a dream report.

A young man in his early twenties comes to his therapeutic hour and reports that he has had the most disturbing dream of his life. The dream, he says, vividly recalls his state of panic at the time of the "mental breakdown" which caused him to enter treatment half a year earlier. He cannot let go of the dream; it seemed painfully real on awakening; and even in the hour of reporting the dream-state seems still vivid enough to threaten the patient's sense of reality. He is afraid that this is the end of his sanity.

The dream: *"There was a big face sitting in a buggy of the horse-and-buggy days. The face was completely empty, and there was horrible, slimy, snaky hair all around it. I am not sure it wasn't my mother."* The dream report itself, given with wordy plaintiveness, is as usual followed by a variety of incidental reports, protestations and exclamations, which at one point give way to a rather coherent account of the patient's relationship with his deceased grandfather, a country parson. Here the patient's mood changes to a deeply moved and moving admission of desperate nostalgia for cultural and personal values once observed and received.

Everything said in this hour is linked, of course, with the material of previous appointments. It must be understood that whatever answer can come of one episode will owe its clarity to the fact that it responds to previous questions and complements previous half-answers. Such *evidential continuity* can be only roughly sketched here; even to account for this one hour would take many hours. Let me briefly state, then, that I listened to the patient, who faced me in an easy chair, with only occasional interruptions for clarification, and that I gave him a résumé of what sense his dream had made to me only at the conclusion of the appointment. It so happened that this interpretation proved convincing to us both and, in the long run, strategic for the whole treatment which, incidentally, ended well.

As I turn to the task of indicating what inferences helped me to formulate one of the most probable of the many possible meanings of this dream report I must ask you to join me in what Freud has called "free-floating attention," an attention which turns inward to the observer's ruminations while remaining turned outward to the field of observation, and which, far from focusing on any one item too intentionally, rather waits to be impressed by recurring themes. These will first faintly but ever more insistently signal the nature of the patient's distress and its location. To find the zone, the position, and the danger I must avoid for the moment all temptations to go off on *one* tangent in order to prove it alone as relevant. It is rather the gradual establishment of strategic intersections on a number of tangents that eventually makes it possible to locate in the observed phenomena that central core which comprises the "evidence."

IV

The patient's behavior and report confront me with a crisis, and it is my first task to perceive where the patient stands in the treatment procedure, and what I must do next. What a clinician must do first and last depends, of course, on the setting of his work. Mine is an open residential institution, working with severe neuroses, on the borderline of psychosis or psychopathy. In such a setting, our patients may display, in their most regressed moments, the milder forms of a disturbance in the sense of reality; in their daily behavior, they usually try to entertain, educate, and employ themselves in rational and useful ways; and in their best moments, they can be expected to be insightful and at times creative. The hospital thus can be said to take a number of risks, and to provide, on the other hand, special opportunities for the patient's abilities to work, to be active, and to share in social responsibilities. That a patient fits into this setting has been established in advance by several weeks of probationary evaluation. During this period the patient's history has been taken in psychiatric interviews with him and perhaps with members of his family; he has been given a physical examination by a physician and has been confronted with standardized tests by psychologists who perform their work "blindly," that is without knowledge of the patient's history; and finally, the results have been presented to the whole staff at a meeting, at the conclusion of which the patient is interviewed by the medical director, questioned by staff members, and assigned to "his therapist." Such preliminary screening has provided the therapist with an over-all diagnosis which defines a certain range of expectable mental states, indicating the patient's special danger points and his special prospects for improvement. Needless to say, not even the best preparation can quite predict what depths and heights may be reached once the therapeutic process gets under way.

A dream report of the kind just mentioned, in a setting of this kind, thus will first of all impress the clinical observer as a diagnostic sign. This is an "anxiety dream." An anxiety dream may happen to anybody, and a mild perseverance of the dream state into the day is not pathological as such. But this patient's dream appears to be only the visual center of a severe affective disturbance: no doubt if such a state were to persist it could precipitate him into a generalized panic such as brought him to our clinic in the first place. The original test report had put the liability of the patient's state into these words: "The tests indicate borderline psychotic features in an inhibited, obsessive-compulsive character. However, the patient seems to be able to take spontaneously adequate distance from these borderline tendencies. He seems, at present, to be struggling to strengthen a rather precarious control over aggressive impulses, and probably feels a good deal of anxiety." The course of the treatment has confirmed this and other test results. The report of this horrible dream which intrudes itself on the patient's waking life now takes its place beside the data of the tests, and the range and spectrum of the patient's moods and states as observed in the treatment, and shows him on the lowest level attained since admission, i.e. relatively closest to an *inability* "to take adequate distance from his borderline tendencies."

The first "prediction" to be made is whether this dream is the sign of an impending collapse, or, on the contrary, a potentially beneficial clinical crisis. The first would mean that the patient is slipping away from me and that I must think, as it were, of the emergency net; the second, that he is reaching out for me with an important message which I must try to understand and answer. I decided for the latter alternative. Although the patient acted as if he were close to a breakdown, I had the impression that, in fact, there was a challenge in all this, and a rather angry one. I can explain this only by presenting a number of inferences of a kind made very rapidly in a clinician's mind, but demonstrable only through an analysis of the patient's verbal and behavioral communications and of my own intellectual and affective reactions.

V

The experienced dream interpreter often finds himself "reading" a dream report as a practitioner of medicine scans an X-ray picture: especially in the cases of wordy or reticent patients or of lengthy case reports, a dream often lays bare the stark inner facts. At this point one may ask: But can *two* clinicians look at the same dream and see the same "stark inner facts"? This is a legitimate question, which I shall try to answer below.

Let us first pay attention to the dream images. The main item is a large face without identifying features. There are no spoken words, and there is no motion. There are no people in the dream. Most apparent then, are omissions. I say this on the basis of an inventory of dream configurations, which I published in a review of "the first dream subjected to exhaustive analysis" by Freud.* Such a methodological step is elementary, but clinical workers often fail to make explicit, even to themselves, what inventories of evidential signs they regularly but unwittingly scan. In my article I suggested a list of configurations against which the student can check the individual dream production for present and absent dream configurations. It must suffice here to indicate that the dream being discussed is characterized by a significant omission of important items present in most dreams: motion, action, people, spoken words. All we have instead is a motionless image of a faceless face, which may or may not represent the patient's mother.

---

* The Dream Specimen of Psychoanalysis," *Journal of the American Psychoanalytic Association*, Volume II, Number 1, January, 1954.

The patient's precarious state and the urgency with which he looked at me when telling me his dream induced me to ignore for the moment the reference to his mother. His facial and tonal expression rather reminded me of a series of critical moments during his treatment when he was obviously not quite sure that I was "all there" and apprehensive that I might disapprove of him and disappear in anger. This focused my attention on a question which the clinician must sooner or later consider when faced with any of his patient's productions, namely, his own place in them.

While the psychotherapist should not force his way into his patient's dream images, sometimes he does well to raise discreetly the masks of the various dream persons to see whether he can find his own face or person or role represented. Here the mask is an empty face, with plenty of horrible hair. My often unruly white hair surrounding a reddish face easily enters my patients' imaginative productions, either as the feature of a benevolent Santa Claus or that of a threatening ogre. At that particular time, I had to consider another autobiographic item. In the third month of therapy, I had "abandoned" the patient to have an emergency operation (which he, to use clinical shorthand, had ascribed to his evil eye, that is to his as yet unverbalized anger). At the time of this dream report I still was on occasion mildly uncomfortable—a matter which can never be hidden from such patients. A sensitive patient will, of course, be in conflict between his sympathy, which makes him want me to take care of myself, and his rightful claim that I should take care of him— for he feels that only the therapist's total presence can provide him with sufficient identity to weather his crises. I concluded that the empty face had something to do with a certain tenuousness in our relation, and that one message of the dream might be something like this: "If I never know whether and when you think of yourself rather than attending to me, or when you will absent yourself, maybe die, how can I have or gain what I need most—a coherent personality, an identity, a face?"

Such an indirect message, however, even if understood as referring to the immediate present and to the therapeutic situation itself, always proves to be "overdetermined," that is, to consist of a condensed code transmitting a number of other messages, from other life situations, seemingly removed from the therapy. This we call "transference."

Among those who are acquainted with this kind of material, some would as a matter of course connect the patient's implied fear of "losing a face" with his remark that he was not sure the face was not his mother's—a double negation easily understood as an affirmation. However, just because the inference of a "mother transference" is at present an almost stereotyped requirement, I should like to approach the whole matter by way of two methodological detours.

VI

Clinical work is always research in progress, and this patient's dream happened to fit especially well into my research at the time. I should say, in passing, that this can be a mixed blessing for the therapeutic contract. A research-minded clinician—and a literary one, as well—must always take care lest his patients become footnotes to his favorite thesis or topic. I was studying in Pittsburgh and in Stockbridge the "identity crises" of a number of young people, college as well as seminary students, workmen and artists. My work was to delineate further a syndrome called *Identity-Diffusion*, a term which describes the inability of young people in the late 'teens and early twenties to establish their station and vocation in life, and the tendency of some to develop apparently malignant symptoms and regressions. Such research must re-open rather than close questions of finalistic diagnosis. Perhaps there are certain stages in the life cycle when even seemingly malignant disturbances are more profitably treated as aggravated life crises rather than as diseases subject to routine psychiatric diagnosis. Here the clinician must be guided by the proposition that if he can hope to save only a small subgroup, or, indeed, only one patient, he must disregard existing statistical verdicts. For one new case, understood in new ways, will soon prove to be "typical" for a class of patients.

But any new diagnostic impression immediately calls for new psychosocial considerations. What we have described as a therapeutic need in one patient, namely, to gain identity by claiming the total presence of his therapist, is analogous with the need of young people anywhere for ideological affirmation. This need is aggravated in certain critical periods of history, when young people may try to find various forms of "confirmation" in groups that range from idealistic youth movements to criminal gangs.

The young man in question was one among a small group of our patients who came from theological seminaries. He had developed his symptoms when attending a Protestant seminary in the Middle West where he was training for missionary work in Asia. He had not found the expected transformation in prayer, a matter which both for reasons of honesty and of inner need, he had taken more seriously than many successful believers. To him the wish to gaze through the glass darkly and to come "face to face" was a desperate need not easily satisfied in some modern seminaries. I need not remind you of the many references in The Bible to God's "making his face to shine upon" man, or God's face being turned away or being distant. The therapeutic theme inferred from the patient's report of an anxiety dream in which a face was horribly unrecognizable thus also seemed to echo relevantly this patient's religious scruples at the time of the appearance of psychiatric symptoms—the common denominator being a wish to break through to a provider of identity.

This detour has led us from the immediate clinical situation to the vocational crisis immediately preceding the patient's breakdown. The "buggy" in the dream will lead us a step further back into the patient's adolescent identity crisis. The horse and buggy is, of course, an historical symbol of culture change. Depending on one's ideology, it is a derisive term connoting hopelessly old-fashioned ways, or it is a symbol of nostalgia for the good old days. Here we come to a trend in the family's history most decisive for the patient's identity crisis. They came from Minnesota where the mother's father had been a rural clergyman of character, strength, and communal esteem. Such grandfathers represent to many men of today a world as yet more homogeneous in its feudal values, masterly and cruel with a good conscience, self-restrained and pious without loss of self-esteem. When the patient's parents had moved from the north country to then still smog-covered Pittsburgh, his mother especially had found it impossible to overcome an intense nostalgia for the rural ways of her youth. She had, in fact, imbued the boy with this nostalgia for a rural existence and had demonstrated marked disappointment when the patient, at the beginning of his identity crisis (maybe in order to cut through the family's cultural conflict) had temporarily threatened to become a hot-rodder and a hep-cat—roles which were beneath the family's "class." The horse and buggy obviously is in greatest ideological as well as technological contrast to the modern means of locomotor acceleration, and, thus, a symbol of changing times, of identity diffusion, and of cultural regression. Here the horrible motionlessness of the dream may reveal itself as an important configurational item, meaning something like being stuck in a world of competitive change and motion. And even as I inferred in my thoughts that the face sitting in the buggy must *also* represent the deceased grandfather's, also framed by white hair, the patient spontaneously embarked on that above-mentioned series of memories concerning the past when his grandfather had taken him by the hand to acquaint him with the technology of an old farm in Minnesota. Here the patient's vocabulary became poetic, his description vivid, and he seemed t ꞏ be breaking through to a genuinely positive emotional experience. Yet his tearfulness remained strangely perverse, almost strangled by anger, as if he were saying: "One must not promise a child such certainty, and then let him down."

I should point out here that as clinicians we consider a patient's "associations" our best leads to the meaning of an item brought up in a clinical encounter. By associated evidence we mean everything which comes to the patient's mind during a clinical session. Here, except in cases of stark disorganization of thought, we must assume that what we call the synthesizing function of the ego will, sometimes with but mostly without conscious knowledge, tend to associate what "belongs together" and condense seemingly separate items into strong images and affects, be the various items ever so remote in history, separate in space, and contradictory in logical terms. Once the therapist has convinced himself of a certain combination in the patient of character, intelligence, and a wish to get well, he can rely on the patient's capacity to produce during a series of therapeutic encounters a sequence of themes, thoughts, and affects which seek their own concordance and provide their own cross-references. It is, of course, this basic synthesizing trend in clinical material itself which permits the clinician to observe with free-floating attention, to refrain from undue interference, and to expect sooner or later a confluence of the patient's search for curative clarification and his own endeavor to recognize meaning and relevance. This expectation is in no way disproved by the fact that much of a clinician's work consists of the recognition and removal of the patient's inner and often unconscious resistances to his own wish to see clearly and to get well. We shall return to this point.

We add to our previous inferences the assumption that the face in the dream is a condensed representation of my face as that of his "doctor" who is not so well himself, and the face of his grandfather, who is now dead and whom as a rebellious youth the patient had defied—in fact, shortly before his death. The immediate clinical situation, then, and the patient's childhood history are found to have a common denominator in the idea that the patient wishes to base his future sanity on a man of wisdom and firm identity while, in both instances, the patient seems to fear that his anger may have destroyed, or may yet destroy, this resource. We have every reason to suspect that some of his insistence on finding security in prayer, and yet his failure to find it, belongs in the same context.

VII

The theme of the horse and buggy as a rural symbol served to establish a possible connection between the nostalgic mother and her dead father; and we now finally turn our attention to the fact that the patient, half-denying what he was half-suggesting, had said, "I am not sure it wasn't my mother." Here the most repetitious complaint of the whole course of therapy must be reviewed. While the grandfather's had been, all in all, the most consistently reassuring countenance in the patient's life, the mother's pretty, soft, and loving face had since earliest childhood been marred in the patient's memory and imagination by moments when she seemed absorbed and distorted by strong and painful emotions. The tests, given before any history-taking, had picked out the following theme: "The mother-figure appears in the Thematic Apperception Tests as one who seeks to control her son by her protectiveness of him, and by 'self-pity' and demonstrations of her frailty at any aggressive act on his part. She is, in the stories, 'frightened' at any show of rebelliousness, and content only when the son is passive and compliant. There appears to be considerable aggression, probably partly conscious, toward this figure." And indeed, it was with anger as well as with horror that the patient would repeatedly describe the mother of his memory as utterly exasperated, and this at those times when he had been too rough, too careless, too stubborn, or too persistent.

We are not concerned here with accusing this actual mother of having behaved this way; we can only be sure that she appeared this way in certain retrospective moods of the patient. Such memories are typical for a class of patients, and the question whether this is so because they have in common a type of mother or a typical reaction to their mothers, or both, occupies the thinking of clinicians. At any rate many of these patients are deeply, if often unconsciously, convinced that they have caused a basic disturbance in their mothers—a disturbance, which, of course, is one of the prime causes rather than an effect of the small child's anxiety and anger. No doubt, in our time, when corporal punishment and severe scolding have become less fashionable, parents resort to the seemingly less cruel means of presenting themselves as deeply hurt by the child's willfulness. The "violated" mother thus has become more prominent in the arsenal of guilt images, and in some cases proves to be a hindrance to the conclusion of adolescence—as if one had to go away back and away down to make an essential restitution before adulthood could be approached. It is in keeping with this trend that the patients under discussion here, young people who in late adolescence face a breakdown of "borderline" proportions, all prove partially regressed to the earliest task in life, namely, that of acquiring a sense of basic trust strong enough to balance that sense of basic mistrust to which newborn man, most dependent of all young animals, and endowed with fewer inborn instinctive regulations, is subject in his infancy. We all relive earlier and earliest stages of our existence in dreams, in artistic experience, and in religious devotion, only to emerge refreshed and invigorated. These patients, however, experience such "partial regression" in a lonely, sudden, and intense fashion, and most of all with a sense of irreversible doom. This, too, is in this dream.

Tracing one main theme of the dream retrospectively, we have recognized it in four periods of the patient's life: the present treatment—and the patient's fear that by some act of horrible anger (on his part or on mine or both) he might lose me and thus his chance to regain his identity through trust in me; his immediately preceding religious education—and his abortive attempt at finding through prayer that "presence" which would cure his inner void; his earlier youth—and his hope to gain strength, peace, and identity by identifying himself with his grandfather; and, finally, early childhood—and his desperate wish to keep alive in himself the charitable face of his mother in order to overcome fear, guilt, and anger over her emotions. Such redundancy points to a central theme which, once found, gives added meaning to all the associated material. The theme is: "Whenever I begin to have faith in somebody's strength and love, some angry and sickly emotions pervade the relationship, and I end up mistrusting, empty, and a victim of anger and despair."

You may be getting a bit tired of the clinician's habit of speaking for the patient, of putting into his mouth inferences which, so it would seem, he could get out of it, for the asking. Perhaps so, but the clinician has no right to test his reconstructions until his trial formulations have combined to a comprehensive interpretation which feels right, and which promises, when appropriately verbalized, to feel right tc the patient. When this point is reached, the clinician usually finds himself compelled to speak.

We have not yet exhausted the categories of thought which must precede such intervention. I have not explicitly stated what my "persuasion," what specifically Freudian concepts of dream life would make me look for in this dream. If according to Freud a successful dream is an attempt at representing a wish as fulfilled, the attempted and miscarried fulfillment in this dream is that of finding a face with a lasting identity. If an anxiety dream startling the dreamer out of his sleep is a symptom of a derailed wish-fulfillment, the central theme just formulated indicates at least one inner disturbance which caused the miscarriage of trust. This becomes even clearer when we come to the mandatory question as to what was the remnant of the previous day which had upset the sleeping patient sufficiently to cause this dream. Why did the patient have this dream on the preceding night, of all nights?

You will not expect me to give an account of the previous day's appointment as well. Suffice it to say that the patient had confessed to increased well-being in work and in love and had expressed enhanced trust in, and even something akin to affection for me. This, paradoxically, his unconscious had not been able to tolerate. The paradox resolves itself if we consider that cure means the loss of the right to rely on therapy; for the cured patient, to speak with Saint Francis, would not so much seek to be loved as to love, and not so much to be consoled as to console, to the limit of his capacity. The dream shocks the patient out of his dangerous increase in self-confidence (and confidence in me) by reminding him of unwise trust and premature graduations in the past. The dream report communicates, protesting somewhat too loudly, that the patient is still sick. We must come to the conclusion that his dream was sicker than the patient was, although his treatment was by no means near conclusion.

A most comprehensive omission in all this material points to what is as yet to come: there is no father in these familial associations. The patient's father images became dominant in a later period of the treatment. You may also have missed a sexual interpretation of the dream. Did not Freud explain the Medusa, the angry face with snake-hair and an open mouth, as a symbol of the feminine void, and an expression of the masculine horror of femininity? It is true that some of the dream material which concerns the mother's emotions, could be easily traced to infantile observations and ruminations concerning "female trouble," pregnancy, and post-partum upsets. Facelessness, in this sense, can also mean inner void, and "castration." Does it, then, or does it not contradict Freudian symbolism, if I emphasize in this equally horrifying but entirely empty face, a representation of facelessness, of loss of face, of lack of identity? In the context of one interpretation, the dream image would be primarily symbolic of a sexual idea which is to be warded off, in the second a representation of a danger to the continuous existence of individual identity (and thus of the "ego"). Theoretical considerations would show that these interpretations can and must be systematically related to one another. In this case the controversy is superseded by the clinical consideration that a symbol is a symbol only when it can be demonstrated to be at work. Furthermore it would be futile to use sexual symbolism dogmatically when acute ego needs can be discerned as dominant in strongly concordant material. The sexual symbolism of this dream was taken up in due time, when it reappeared in another context, namely that of manhood and sexuality, and revealed the bisexual confusion inherent in all identity diffusion.

Controversies in regard to the therapeutic priority of particular interpretations can in principle be settled in discussions along the evidential lines sketched in this paper. However, since interpretation in this field must deal systematically with motivations which often are the more unconscious the more compelling they are, the whole area of evidential consensus is apt to be beclouded with age-old defensive attitudes of belief and disbelief. On the one hand, psychotherapists themselves are apt to solidify transient controversies in "schools" of thought which make dogmas out of theories and mark skepticism as resistance and unbelief, thus (unconsciously) using traditional methods of meeting the unknown where it is most personal. On the other hand, in the field of man's motivation, insights already firmly gained are forever subject to renewed repression and denial. It is in the very nature of man's intelligence that it can serve both the rational approaches to the facts of nature and also the rationalization and disguise of man's own nature. Therefore, in dealing with the *sense of evidence* in clinical matters, we must accept irrational belief as well as irrational disbelief as part of an inescapable dilemma which calls for a new kind of disciplined self-awareness.

VIII

So much for inferences concerning the meaning of the dream. It is not necessary in this presentation to insist that all of this and infinitely more can go through a clinician's head fast enough to make him react to the patient's behavior with whatever skillful determination is at his disposal. I may now confess that the initial invitation really requested me to tell you "how a *good* clinician works." I have replaced this embarrassing little word with dots until now when I can make it operational. It marks the good clinician that much can go on in him without clogging his communication at the moment of therapeutic intervention, when only the central theme may come to his awareness. On the other hand, he must also be able to call it all to explicit awareness when the circumstances permit the time to spell it out—for how else could such thinking be disciplined, shared and taught? Such sharing and teaching, however, if it is to transcend clinical impressionism, presupposes a communality of conceptual approaches. I cannot give you today more than a mere inkling that there is a systematic relationship between clinical observation on the one hand and, on the other, such conceptual points of view as Freud has introduced into psychiatry: a *structural* point of view denoting a kind of anatomy of the mind, a *dynamic* point of view denoting a kind of physiology of mental forces and of their transformations and, finally, a *genetic* point of view reconstructing the differentiation during distinct childhood stages of an inner organization and of certain energy transformations. But even as such propositions are tested on a wide front of inquiry (from the direct observation of children and perception experiments to "metapsychological" discussion), it stands to reason that clinical evidence is characterized by a human immediacy which transcends formulations ultimately derived from mechanistic patterns of thought.

To enlarge on this would lead me to the question of the collaboration of the clinician and the theoretician. Let me, instead, return to the problem of how, having perused all the above in his own mind, the clinician prepares for therapeutic intervention. For we have postulated that such intervention and the patient's reactions to it are an integral part of the evidence provided in the therapeutic encounter. Therapists of different persuasions differ as to what constitutes an interpretation: an impersonal and authoritative explanation, a warm and fatherly suggestion, an expansive sermon or a sparse encouragement to go on and see what comes up next. In each case, however, the tone of the interpretation will be influenced by the therapist's emotions, of which the patient is anxiously aware.

The preferred mode of interpretation (and this is the second prediction to be made in a clinical encounter) in our case necessarily included a relatively explicit statement of the therapist's emotional response to the dream report. Patients of the type of our young man, still smarting in his twenties under what he considered his mother's strange emotions in his infancy, can learn to delineate social reality and to tolerate emotional tension only if the therapist can juxtapose his own emotional reactions -hopefully more disciplined—to the patient's emotions. Therefore, as I reviewed with the patient in brief words most of what I have put before you, I was also able to tell him without anger, but not without some indignation, that my response to his account had included some feeling of anger. I explained that he had worried me, had made me feel pity, had touched me with his memories, and had burdened me with the proof, all at once, of the goodness of mothers, of the immortality of grandfathers, of my own perfection, and of God's grace. The demonstration that anger can be raised to the level of an educative and self-educative indignation is a not irrelevant by-product of many an interpretation.

The words used in an interpretation, however, are hard to remember and when reproduced often sound as arbitrary as any private language developed by two people in the course of an intimate association. Let me, therefore, state a generality instead. A good therapeutic interpretation, while often brief and simple in form, should be based on an implicit theme such as I have put before you, a theme common at the same time to a dominant trend in the patient's relation to the therapist, to a significant portion of his symptomatology, to an important period of his childhood, and to corresponding facets of his work and love-life. Although all of these trends may seem to be disparate enough further to bewilder the patient upon confrontation, clinical experience proves otherwise: they *are* (as I must repeat in conclusion) very closely related to each other in the patient's own struggling ego, for which the traumatic past is of course a present frontier, perceived as acute conflict. Such an interpretation, therefore, joins the patient's and the therapist's modes of problem-solving.

The intervention in this case, however, highlights one methodological point truly unique to clinical work, namely, the disposition of the clinician's "mixed" feelings, his emotions and opinions. The evidence is not "all in" if he does not succeed in using his own emotional responses during a clinical encounter as an evidential source and as a guide in intervention, instead of putting them aside with a spurious claim to unassailable objectivity. It is here that the requirement of the therapist's own psychoanalytic treatment as a didactic experience proves itself as essential, for the personal equation in the observer's emotional response is as important in psychotherapy as that of the senses in the laboratory. Repressed emotions easily hide themselves in the therapist's most stubborn blind spots.

What do we expect the patient to contribute to the closure of such evidence? What tells us that our interpretation was "right," and, therefore, made the evidence as conclusive as it can be in our kind of work? The simplest answer is that this particular patient was delighted when I told him of my thoughts and of my anger over his unnecessary attempts to burden me with a future which he could well learn to manage—a statement which was not meant to be a therapeutic "suggestion," a clinical slap on the back, but was based on what I knew of his inner resources as well as of the use he made of the opportunities offered in our clinical community. The patient left the hour—which he had begun with a sense of dire disaster—with a broad smile and obvious encouragement. In a most immediate way, this could be said to "clinch" the evidence; at least it shows that our predictions had not gone wildly astray.

I think I have outlined the rationale for my action and the patient's reaction. He had taken a chance with himself and with me, I thought. Under my protection and the hospital's he had hit bottom by chancing a repetition of his original breakdown. He had gone to the very border of unreality and had gleaned from it a highly condensed and seemingly anarchic image. I had shown him that the image, while experienced like a symptom, was in fact a kind of creation, or at any rate a condensed and highly meaningful communication and challenge, for which my particular clinical theory had made me receptive enough to be able to "talk back" without hesitation. A sense of mutuality and reality was thus restored, reinforced by the fact that while accepting his transferences as meaningful, I had refused to become drawn into them. I played neither mother, grandfather, nor God (this is the hardest), but had offered him my help as defined by my professional status in attempting to understand what was behind his helplessness. By relating the fact that his underlying anger aroused mine, and that I could say so without endangering either myself or him, I could show him that in his dream he had also confronted anger in the image of a Medusa—a Gorgon which, neither of us being a hero, we could yet slay together.

IX

This, then, is an example which ends on a convincing note, leaving both the patient and the practitioner with the feeling that they are a pretty clever pair. If it were always required to clinch a piece of clinical evidence in this manner, we should have few convincing examples. To demonstrate other kinds, however, would take other hours.

Undoubtedly some may be inclined to interpret what I have reported in a different way. Against such a contingency, I can only claim (and hope to have demonstrated) that there is enough method in our work systematically to force favorite assumptions to become probable inferences by cross-checking them diagnostically, genetically, structurally, and in a number of other ways, all sufficiently systematized to allow for orderly discussion. Furthermore, in the long run, clinical evidence consists of a series of such encounters as I have outlined here, the series being characterized by a concomitantly progressive or regressive shift in all the areas mentioned.

Clinical training essentially consists of the charting of such series. In each step, our auxiliary methods must help us to work with reasonable precision and with the courage to revise our assumptions and our techniques systematically, if and when the clinical evidence should show that we overestimated or underestimated the patient or ourselves, the chances waiting for him in his environment, or the usefulness of our particular discipline.

In order to counteract such subjectivity and selectivity as I have put before you today, whole treatments are now being sound-filmed so that qualified secondary observers can follow the procedure. This may be important in some lines of research, and advantageous in training; yet, it is obvious that this process only puts a second observer in the position to decide, on the basis of his reactions and selections, whether or not he agrees with the judgments made by the original observer on the basis of his unrecorded and unrecordable reactions and selections; all the while, between the recording and the analysis of the data, history will be found to have marched on.

Neither will the nature of clinical evidence change in such new developments as *group-psychotherapy*, where a therapist faces a group of patients and they face one another as well as him, permitting a number of combinations and variations of the basic elements of a clinical encounter. Clinical evidence, finally, will be much enhanced but not changed in nature by a sharpened awareness (such as now emanates from *sociological studies*) of the psychotherapist's as well as the patient's position in society and history.

It is in this historical connection that we may return to the fate of the word "clinical." The individualistic character of my specimen and of our conceptual framework will be found to have their most explicit opposite in the practices and theories in the Communist part of the world, where different views are held regarding neuroses (they are taken to be a matter of nerves, subject to neurological treatment); regarding psychiatry proper; and finally, regarding the asocial and, in a sense, amoral aspects of some emotional disturbance. In the Far East, the word "clinical" is again assuming an entirely different historical connotation, insofar as it concerns mind at all: in Communist China the "thought analyst" faces individuals considered to be in need of reform. He encourages sincere confessions and self-analyses in order to realign thoughts with "the people's will." It will be interesting to learn more by comparison about the ideological implications of concepts of mental sickness, of social deviancy, and of psychological cure.

The ideological relativity implicit in clinical work may, to some, militate against its scientific value. I could not indicate in this paper what can be gleaned from clinical theory and application. I could only try to give an introduction to the clinician's basic view which asserts that you may learn about the nature of things as you find out what you can do *with* them, but that the true nature of man reveals itself only in the attempt to do something *for* him.

Evidence and Inference
in Nuclear Research

MARTIN DEUTSCH

TIME AND AGAIN the question of evidence and inference in experimental physics has been used as a starting point for the discussion of scientific method. I shall discuss the question in a rather personal way, for in my own work I have been puzzled at times by the striking degree to which an experimenter's preconceived image of the process which he is investigating determines the outcome of his observations. The image to which I refer is the symbolic anthropomorphic representation of the basically inconceivable atomic processes.

Modern microphysics deals with phenomena on a scale on which there are no human sense organs to permit a direct perception of the phenomena investigated. I do not mean simply that our organs are not sensitive enough to observe the processes. This would be true in astronomy, where the observed celestial bodies may be too far away to be seen and resolved by the human eye, and in geology, where the interior of the earth is not accessible to direct observation. In quantum physics, however, the inaccessibility is of a more fundamental nature. While telescopes and microscopes and seismological listening devices can refine our senses to the point where they will give a sensory impression of the astronomical or microscopic objects which, although distorted, is still certainly relevant, there is no conceivable way of seeing, for example, an electron in its orbit in the hydrogen atom, or a neutron on its way out of a nucleus.

The human imagination, including the creative scientific imagination, can ultimately function only by evoking potential or imagined sense impressions. I cannot prove that the statement I have just made is absolutely true, but I have never met a physicist, at least not an experimental physicist, who does not think of the hydrogen atom by evoking a visual image of what he would see if the particular atomic model with which he is working existed literally on a scale accessible to sense impressions. At the same time the physicist realizes that in fact the so-called internal structure of the hydrogen atom is *in principle* inaccessible to direct sensory perception. This situation has far-reaching consequences for the method of experimental investigation. The use in the interpretation of physical phenomena of factors not directly perceivable is, of course, very old. But there is a basic difference between this procedure in classical phenomena and in microscopic quantum physics—a difference which I shall try to illustrate by two examples.

First let me take a classical example, the simple meteorological phenomenon of the rising and setting of the sun. There is probably immediate agreement among all rational observers of the sun's behavior, that we are dealing with the relative motion in space of a luminous body and the observer. (Only very rarely has the suggestion been made that we are really dealing with a stationary object and that only the light rays follow different paths in the course of the day.) The nature of this motion has been investigated by methods familiar to every schoolboy. The angle at which the sun is visible from various locations at various times has been recorded with great care and compared with the angle at which the moon and the stars are visible. Various kinematic descriptions have been achieved, such as the Ptolemaic and Copernican. Further refinement of such theories have led to a dynamic rather than kinematic description, in terms of the Newtonian system of gravitational mechanics appropriately modified by relativity. Whatever theory we may develop, there will never be any doubt that the relevant observations are those of the sun's position, of the length of shadows, etc. There is a direct and self-evident link between the sensory image and the scientific theory.

But now let us consider one theory of celestial mechanics which has at various times enjoyed great popularity: we assume that the sun is moved by a spirit which may be appeased or influenced to act in a favorable or unfavorable fashion. For example, the rising of the sun must be achieved by invoking the favor of this spirit. To test this theory our experimentation has to apply not only to the sun, the moon, the stars, and the shadows, but in principle also to the spirit which is not amenable to sensory perception. The whole context of relevant factors is now suddenly changed; if the sun is eclipsed it may become necessary to investigate whether the king did not violate a taboo. Furthermore, the question is really very difficult to settle by experimentation because the spirit might at one time be in a more tolerant mood than at another and we have, in principle, no way of making this mood directly accessible to our senses.

Bad though this situation is, it is in some respects more favorable than that obtaining in quantum physics. It is, after all, ultimately possible to decide between these theories with reasonable certainty by performing observations only on the celestial bodies themselves. Having accumulated a sufficient amount of data concerning the behavior of the sun over the centuries, we arrive at a complete description of past and future phenomena based entirely on direct sensory observations, and the animist theories collapse from the lack of evidence for their relevance rather than because they are explicitly disproved. The evidence is convincing for any person with an ordinary degree of imagination, i.e., an ordinary ability to evoke the sense impressions which he would receive from the sun under certain specified conditions.

In a typical modern physics experiment, on the other hand, the direct sensory impressions of the experimental situation are not only not very helpful to the solution of the problem investigated, but are not even likely to reveal the relevant factors. A typical high-energy physics laboratory abounds in impressive sights and sounds. There is likely to be the huge magnet of an accelerator, pounding periodically as it is energized, the whirr of the electric generators, perhaps clouds of condensation above containers of liquid air and the rushing cooling water. The control room and the experimental area are filled with colored lights, hundreds of knobs, moving meter needles, and flashing oscilloscope patterns to delight the heart of the space child.

I am sure that a scientist of 150 years ago, told to proceed with experimentation in this laboratory, would have no difficulty in making extensive observations on the change in the appearance of the lights as various knobs are turned, and on the variation in the pitch of the generator noise. But, of course, none of these changes directly accessible to sensory impression are really relevant to the experiment actually being carried out. Even in the very roughest, preliminary experiment the nuclear physicist does not look at the object of his investigation, or listen to it, or sniff it, or try to determine its temperature. He does not start with a simple impression of the phenomena, later refined by quantitative measurement. The only visible feature intimately connected with the actual experiment may be the position of a knob controlling the current through a magnet and a mechanical recording device indicating the rate of arrival of electrical signals from a small counter. The experimental procedure may consist simply in noting the reading on the recorder as a function of the magnet current. Both the change made—the position of the control knob—and the resulting effect—the reading on the recorder—seem almost negligible in the totality of material involved in the experiment.

This is also true if we search a little deeper and consider the total energy or total electric current involved in the actual observation, and compare it with the totals involved in the experiment. To make matters worse, there are probably several other knobs which could be turned with much more drastic effect on our recorder. In addition, there are literally dozens of similar recording devices and hundreds of other similar knobs connected with the experiment, some of which may show correlations much more marked than those under investigation. Yet, if you ask the experienced experimenter he may tell you that these other effects are either fully understood or certainly without importance. We see, then, a situation in which the experiment is carried out under conditions in which almost all sensory impressions concerning its operation are irrelevant to the question investigated and in which a large number of related phenomena remain uninvestigated and, therefore, unexplained.

How is it possible that important and reliable conclusions are drawn from this experimentation? The answer lies in the fact that the experimenter starts out with a well structured image of the actual connections between the events taking place. Far from approaching the problem with the completely open mind which is supposed to be characteristic of the scientist investigating in an unbiased fashion all possible connections, he starts with the conviction that all of the relevant occurrences except the one which he is actually investigating in the experiment are either fully understood or at least in principle explicable on the basis of the preconceived image. Without this image, the experiment certainly could not have been conceived in the first place.

In terms of our current image its description might be as follows: when the high-energy proton beam produced in the accelerator strikes the nuclei of the beryllium target, mesons are produced by the impact of these protons on the beryllium nuclei. They emerge from the target at various angles with various velocities. A narrow beam of these mesons is allowed to pass through a deflecting magnet and then through two particle detectors placed several meters apart. We determine the velocity of the mesons in terms of the measurable time interval between the electrical pulses indicating their passage through the first and second of the detecting counters mentioned. The angle through which a beam of charged particles is deflected by a magnet of given strength is determined by the particles' momentum (classically, the product of its mass and its velocity). Since the particles can enter the detecting counters only if they have been deflected through a specified angle, the counters record only particles of a fixed momentum. Having measured the momentum and the velocity, we can directly calculate the mass. By changing the magnet current we vary this momentum until it corresponds to the velocity selected by the counters.

If one does not already have some familiarity with the field, this very condensed description is probably not sufficient to form a clear image of the experiment. But I hope that it does give the feeling that with the aid of a few simple diagrams and perhaps a clarification of some of the concepts involved, there would be no difficulty in understanding the result of this kind of measurement. The only reason for the acceptance of this picture by non-physicists is, however, the good name of the physicist who presents the picture. I cannot actually show you the protons, the nuclei, the mesons or even the electrical impulses except in an indirect fashion which already involves a good part of the conclusions to be understood.

Similar problems arise also in other fields when a certain degree of sophistication has been reached, but I believe that the intellectual ocean between the actual observation and its rational interpretation which must be crossed by "dead reckoning" creates special problems for the experimental physicist. It is much safer and easier to change direction and to explore all possibilities while sailing on a lake within sight of the shores than it is while navigating an uncharted ocean, where even the sun and the stars are no longer visible. I have attempted to demonstrate that the actual phenomena, the actual physical occurrences in the apparatus of the typical modern experiment, are extremely complex, and many of them involve interactions vastly greater than those under investigation. It is therefore of vital importance to consider not only the desired effects, but also as many of the alternative influences as possible. This is, of course, at the very core of experimental scientific procedure.

There is no recipe, no rule of procedure which will permit the unimaginative experimenter to consider all of these possibilities by applying systematic logical analysis to all aspects of his apparatus. The only workable scheme is to operate within the framework of an anthropomorphic image. It is sometimes amusing to watch two highly competent physicists discuss the functioning of an apparatus if their images have for some reason taken somewhat different forms; despite the fact that they reach the same conclusions they may have some difficulty communicating with each other.

I should really say that there are two separate images involved in most experiments, one image representing the functioning of the apparatus, the other the basic physical phenomenon investigated. The procedure is probably more familiar in the instrumental aspect. We structure the behavior of the complicated physical phenomena according to a functional interpretation; that is, we consider each part of the apparatus as a unit having a definite function with respect to our purpose. The language which we apply to it is frequently ludicrously anthropomorphic. For example, we say without hesitation: "This amplifier does not *like* to operate at high counting rates," or "This circuit is designed to *reject* protons." The functional image which we construct is more sophisticated than this would imply, but it also ultimately reduces the functioning of the apparatus to terms analogous to phenomena directly amenable to sensory verification. This functional view of the physical phenomena does not cause any serious complications when applied to the apparatus. After all, the apparatus is designed to perform a certain function according to the desire of the experimenter, and while there may be aspects of its behavior which cannot be understood within this image, these are not necessarily relevant to the experiment.

The problem is very much more serious when we consider the image representing the fundamental physical phenomenon studied. The description which I gave at the outset of the experiment that has been discussed is certainly not the only possible one of the sequence of events. We could, for example, imagine the phenomenon as one of interaction between the beryllium target, struck by the protons in our accelerator, and certain atoms in our counters. The concept of an unobservable physical particle traveling in a well-defined path through the magnet would then not be part of the image. We clearly could not have designed our original experiment and measured the mass of the particle unless we had started out with an image of the phenomenon involving such a "particle." The very word used implies the image.

But a meson is clearly not an object with the general properties of a ball which we could see if we had a sufficiently good microscope, or feel impinging on our hand if our nerves were a little more sensitive. We are not forced by direct sensory perception to use this image. We have developed it because it allows us to reason from one experiment to the next by analogy; even in a mathematically sophisticated theory we deal with formal thought processes designed to connect sensory impressions. It, too, must proceed by analogy with the connections established between such perceivable events.

Now it is clear that if one is too strongly attached to one's preconceived model, one will of necessity miss all radical discoveries. It is amazing to what degree one may fail to register mentally an observation which does not fit the initial image. I could quote some sad examples from my own career. On the other hand, if one is too open-minded and pursues every hitherto unknown phenomenon, one is almost certain to lose oneself in trivia.

As I have tried to show in my illustration, in a typical experiment in modern physics the apparatus involves complex influences frequently of much greater order of magnitude than the phenomenon investigated. Each of these influences can occupy a lifetime of experimental investigation before it is fully understood, and is most likely to be of no particular scientific interest as it concerns only features of a particular piece of apparatus. The ability to distinguish between what we call colloquially a "dirt effect" and a basic phenomenon that is still an unknown is what constitutes the decisive intuition of the experimenter in this field. It is really the ability to recognize relevance in the evidence presented by the experiment.

I believe that there are at least three different manners of experimentation in modern physics. While the three approaches may employ almost identical techniques in detail, they imply differences in attitude on the part of the experimenter. Most creative physicists show a definite tendency to favor one or the other of these approaches, at least during a large part of their active career. Most physicists also have a very strong prejudice about the relative merit or creative stature of the different approaches, although there is no general agreement concerning the order of such merit. Each approach has made great and decisive contributions to our knowledge and understanding.

The first of these three types of experimentation might be called "observation." It is the type we normally associate with the naturalist, a manner of letting nature bring the questions and answers to you. The phenomenon to be investigated may be ill-defined at the outset, and the interpretation of the result obtained is initially uncertain. It is at this point that the investigator's imagination and ingenuity are applied. In this type of experiment the image or model enters least consciously. In fact, the sophisticated model with its mathematical refinements is avoided as far as possible. The experimenter wants to approach the phenomena in what he considers to be the most unbiased fashion.

But it is not possible to analyze and design an experiment without recourse to an image. Hence the experimenter will tentatively order his results according to a deliberately more primitive sensory image. He prefers so-called "visual techniques," of which the classical and still widely used example is the Wilson Cloud Chamber. Here, ionizing particles leave vapor tracks which are photographed; from the density, curvature and branching of these tracks the experts deduce the details of nuclear events which have taken place in the chamber, much as the auspex observed the flight of birds and the gypsy studies the pattern of tea leaves to predict the future. These methods give the illusion of direct sensory perception of the events involved. In fact, the relation between this sensory impression and the fundamental physical phenomenon may not be simple. It does, however, permit a logical analysis of the results without reference to the more sophisticated images required when one's reasoning is more closely linked with the actual physical process. Even when visual techniques are not used, this type of experimenter will usually like direct sensory representation of the results. You will find him representing his results as curves or graphs and squinting at these pictures in an attempt to relate himself in some way to the outstanding visual features.

The field of cosmic rays has long attracted physicists whose natural bent favors this kind of experimentation. Cosmic rays present themselves with an intensity and a variety which cannot be controlled by the experimenter, who can only design his apparatus to observe what arrives from outer space. An outstanding result of this type of experimentation was the discovery by C. D. Anderson and, independently, by J. C. Street of the μ-meson, a particle of a kind completely unknown and unexpected at the time. The discovery was based on the appearance of a few cloud-chamber tracks produced by cosmic radiation. This first type of experiment leads most frequently to the kind of success to which the word discovery is most appropriately applied, namely, a new knowledge or insight found in an unexpected place or context.

The second type of experiment is the one which the layman most generally expects to hear reported; starting with a well-established theory or perhaps with two alternative and mutually exclusive theories, the experimenter designs conditions in which the theory predicts a definite qualitative or quantitative outcome in a manner such that a contradictory result would require a basic revision of the theory or the acceptance of one of the two alternative theories and rejection of the other. In other words, the experimenter designs a "test" for the theory.

The ideal experiment of this type is one in which the decision can be reached from the qualitative outcome and depends very little on the precision of the measurement or the perfection of the experimental technique. This condition is of course rarely met in actual experiments, but the ingenuity of the experimenter in this situation is applied to the design of an experiment approaching these characteristics. We see clearly how this differs from the first, "observation" type of experiment; in the "test" the phenomenon studied is determined by the pre-existing theory, and the interpretation of the results should be self-evident in a well-designed experiment. The experimenter's contribution lies in the invention of a sharply defined experiment.

In this "test" type of experiment, the image enters most consciously and explicitly. In fact, the experiment is usually designed to test the applicability of the image. Several of the most decisive advances in atomic and nuclear physics have been achieved by this type of experiment. The most recent and one of the most beautiful examples is the experiment by Wu, Ambler, Hudson, and Hayward, which proved the Lee-Yang theory postulating the breakdown of parity conservation in weak interactions. This theory had been developed as a tentative interpretation of some other experiments of the "observation" type dealing with heavy mesons. A number of workers were attempting to test this theory by means of experiments which required high precision of measurement. The results had been indecisive. The beauty of the decisive experiment lay in the fact that it produced a large effect which did not have to be measured with great precision. Provided the apparatus was performing at all as intended, the result of the experiment was incontrovertible.

The third type of experiment is of the kind which I should like to designate "measurement." Here the experimenter accepts the framework and perhaps even the details of the theory for the phenomena which he investigates. He may proceed to determine a constant of nature, as in the classic Millikan oil-drop experiment. Or he may investigate specific cases not easily fully investigated in the theory. A large part of atomic and nuclear spectroscopy falls into this category.

In this type of experiment the role of the image is harder to assess. In one sense, the experiment is frequently designed on the assumption of the validity of the image. For example, the experiment which we have described above can only measure the mass of the meson if the image of the meson as a "particle" is valid. On the other hand, this type of experiment is, in some respects, the most naive and straightforward observation of the physical phenomena and a quantitative experimental result of the experiment may be found to be incompatible with the image or theory on which the measurement was based. At some point, frequently almost by accident, a phenomenon is observed which simply cannot be understood in terms of the established image.

A classic example of this occurrence is the famous Davison-Germer experiment. This experiment was designed to study the paths of electrons conceived of as particles in the sense of the classical model when they are scattered from crystals. The observations could not readily be ordered and understood in terms of this particle image at all. They seemed much more reminiscent of results obtained in phenomena to which an image of waves was customarily applied. The result of this classic experiment then was the acceptance, already foreshadowed by other developments, of another image in which we think of electrons in the manner in which we usually think of waves.

I have myself in most of my work preferred to perform this kind of experiment. We have always been encouraged by a remark of Enrico Fermi: "Go ahead and perform this experiment. If you are lucky, you will make a discovery; if you have bad luck and your results agree with existing theory, you have at least performed a measurement." It is of course the ambition of every experimenter performing this kind of experiment to make a discovery, somehow to sail safely between the Scylla of intellectual prejudice which makes us reject evidence not readily integrated without preconceived notions, and the Charybdis of irrelevance which has swallowed many working days spent in the pursuit of instrumental artifacts.

Evidence and Inference in Social Research[°]

Paul F. Lazarsfeld

IN RECENT decades a major development of quantitative research in real social situations has come about; in a very broad sense it may be labeled "survey research." The following discussion is concerned with several recurring and very general problems connected with this type of work.

Concentration on survey research does not underrate the importance of other techniques. The same period has seen a similar development in the use of experimental methods in the social sciences; but the logical problems of experiments here and in the natural sciences are essentially the same. There is also a long tradition of social analysis using historical data to study problems of large-scale social change—the relation of the Protestant Reformation to the rise of capitalism is the most famous example. This kind of study raises interesting logical problems of its own that need careful analysis, but the methodology of "historical sociology" is not yet developed enough to be discussed here. Finally there are the attempts to derive social inferences from institutional data. It has been said that man is a data-producing animal. Wherever he goes he leaves certain kinds of data—court records, tax records, school records, birth and death records, and the like. This leads to the possibility of using existing institutional data as indicators of complex social trends and relationships. Durkheim's use of suicide rates to study problems of social norms and social cohesion is the classic example here.

Studies of the type with which we shall be concerned, however, have three distinctive features: they are quantitative rather than qualitative; the researcher designs and uses his own data-gathering devices rather than depending on available historical or institutional records; and they concern people's behavior and attitudes in real-life situations rather than constructed experimental situations.

* Publication No. A-276 of the Bureau of Applied Social Research, Columbia University. I am indebted to Prof. Allen Barton and Mr. Herbert Menzel for their contributions to this review.

From the point of view of this group of papers, two topics deserve special attention. How are broad conceptual ideas converted into instruments of empirical research to provide evidence on a topic of inquiry? And how can the "variables" so developed be manipulated to lead to broader generalizations? Both these problems need much additional specification. For the first we shall pay special attention to two issues: What happens if we have a choice between several instruments? And what happens if our evidence pertains to both individuals and collectives—a topic of traditional interest to the social scientist? As far as inference goes, social research has brought two topics to the foreground: how can we come near to causal relations, if we have no experiments but descriptive data only? And what hope can we place on the role of mathematics in the social sciences? The following five sections will briefly discuss these topics.

I. THE FLOW FROM CONCEPTS TO EMPIRICAL INDICES

No science deals with its objects of study in their full concreteness. It selects certain of their properties and attempts to establish relations among them. The finding of such laws is the ultimate goal of all scientific inquiries. But in the social sciences the singling out of relevant properties is in itself a major problem. No standard terminology has yet been developed for this task. The properties are sometimes called aspects or attributes, and often the term "variable" is borrowed from mathematics as the most general category. The attribution of properties is interchangeably called description, classification, or measurement.

When social scientists use the term "measurement," it is in a much broader sense than the natural scientists do. For instance, if we are able to say that one department in a company has higher morale than another, we would be very pleased with ourselves and we would say that we had performed a "measurement." We would not worry that we cannot say that it is twice as high or only 20 per cent higher. This does not mean that we make no efforts to arrive at measurements in the traditional sense, with a precise metric. Some success has been achieved, but these efforts are only beginning, and they represent merely a small part of measurement activities in the broader sense.

Keeping in mind this generalized idea of measurement, let us see how social scientists establish devices by which to characterize the objects of empirical investigations. There appears to be a typical process which recurs regularly when we establish "variables" for measuring complex social objects. This process by which concepts are translated into empirical indices has four steps: an initial imagery of the concept, the specification of dimensions, the selection of observable indicators, and the combination of indicators into indices.

1. Imagery. The flow of thought and analysis and work which ends up with a measuring instrument usually begins with something which might be called imagery. Out of the analyst's immersion in all the detail of a theoretical problem, he creates a rather vague image or construct. The creative act may begin with the perception of many disparate phenomena as having some underlying characteristic in common. Or the investigator may have observed certain regularities and is trying to account for them. In any case, the concept, when first created, is some vaguely conceived entity that makes the observed relations meaningful.

Suppose we want to study industrial firms. We naturally want to measure the management of the firm. What do we mean by management and managers? Is every foreman a manager? Somewhere the notion of management was started, within a man's writing or a man's experience. Someone noticed that, under the same conditions, sometimes a factory is well run and sometimes it is not well run. Something was being done to make men and materials more productive. This "something" was called management, and ever since students of industrial organization have tried to make this notion more concrete and precise.

The same process happens in other fields. By now the development of intelligence tests has become a large industry. But the beginning of the idea of intelligence was that, if you look at little boys, some strike you as being alert and interesting and others as dull and uninteresting. This kind of general impression starts the wheels rolling for a measurement problem.

2. Concept specification. The next step is to take this original imagery and divide it into components. The concept is specified by an elaborate discussion of the phenomena out of which it emerged. We develop "aspects," "components," "dimensions," or similar specifications. They are sometimes derived logically from the over-all concept, or one aspect is deduced from another, or empirically observed correlations between them are reported. The concept is shown to consist of a complex combination of phenomena, rather than a simple and directly observable item.

Suppose you want to know if a production team is efficient. You have a beginning notion of efficiency. Somebody comes and says, "What do you really mean? Who are more efficient—those who work quickly and make a lot of mistakes, so that you have many rejections, or those who work slowly but make very few rejects?" You might answer, depending on the product, "Come to think of it, I really mean those who work slowly and make few mistakes." But do you want them to work so slowly that there are no rejects in ten years? That would not be good either. In the end you divide the notion of efficiency into components such as speed, good product, careful handling of the machines—and suddenly you have what measurement theory calls a set of dimensions.

The development of dimensions can go quite far. One university in California has made a study under a Navy contract of an airplane factory, aimed at determining what is really efficient management on the lowest level. The notion of efficient management was divided into nineteen components, some of which were: absence of dissensions in the group, good communication downward, not too much compulsion, consistency of command, the size of command, and so on.

This can probably be overdone. I have rarely seen a concept that needed nineteen dimensions. But as a general principle, every concept we use in the social sciences is so complex that breaking it down into dimensions is absolutely essential in order to translate it into any kind of operation or measurement.

3. Selection of indicators. After we have decided on these dimensions, there comes the third step: finding indicators for the dimensions. Here we run into a number of problems. First of all, how does one "think up" indicators? The problem is an old one.

William James has written in *The Meaning of Truth:*

. . . Suppose, e.g., that we say a man is prudent. Concretely, that means that he takes out insurance, hedges in betting, looks before he leaps . . . As a constant habit in him, a permanent tone of character, it is convenient to call him prudent in abstraction from any one of his acts. . . . There are peculiarities in his psychophysical system that make him act prudently. . . .

Here James proceeds from an image to a series of indicators suggested directly by common experience. Today we would be rather more specific about the relation of these indicators to the underlying quality. We would not expect a prudent man always to hedge in betting, or to take out insurance on all possible risks; instead we would talk about the probability that he will perform any specific act as compared with a less prudent individual. And we would know that the indicators might vary considerably, depending on the social setting of the individual. Among students in a Protestant denominational college, for instance, we might find little betting and rare occasions for taking out insurance. Still a measure of prudence could be devised which was relevant to the setting. We might use as indicators whether a student always makes a note before he lends a book, whether he never leaves his dormitory room unlocked, etc.

The fact that each indicator has not an absolute but only a probability relation to our underlying concept requires us to consider a great many possible indicators. The case of intelligence tests furnishes an example. First, intelligence is divided into dimensions of manual intelligence, verbal intelligence, and so on. But even then there is not just one indicator by which imaginativeness can be measured. We must use many indicators to get at it.

There is hardly any observation which has not at one time or another been used as an indicator of something we want to measure. We use a man's salary as one of the indicators of his ability; but we do not rely on it exclusively, or we would have to consider most businessmen more able than even top-ranking university professors. We take the number of patients a doctor has cured as another indicator of ability in that setting; but we know that a good surgeon is more likely to lose a patient than is a good dermatologist. We take the number of books in a public library as an indicator of the cultural level of the community; but we know that quality of books matters as much as quantity.

When a battery of indicators is being drawn up, one difficult problem is to decide where to stop. Which indicators are considered "part of" the concept, and which are considered independent of or external to it? If we start listing indicators of the "integration" of a community, is the crime rate a part of the conception of integration, or is it an external factor which we might try to predict from our measure of integration? Here again, as with the problem of projective indices, knowing the laws which relate indicators to one another is of great importance. Even if we exclude crime rates from our image of an "integrated" city, they might be so highly correlated, as a matter of empirical generalization, that we could use them as a measure of integration in situations where we could not get data on the indicators which we "really" want to call integration. To do this, of course, we must first have "validating studies" where we correlate crime rate with the other indicators of integration and establish that it is generally closely related. We should also know whether there are other factors besides integration influencing crime rate which might confuse our measurements if we used it alone to measure integration, so that we can check on these other factors, or add enough other indicators so as to cancel out their influence.

4. Formation of indices. The fourth step is to put Humpty Dumpty together again. After the efficiency of a team or intelligence of a boy has been divided into six dimensions, and ten indicators have been selected for each dimension, we have to put them all together, because we cannot operate with all those dimensions and indicators separately.

For some situations we have to make one over-all index out of them. If I have six students and only one fellowship to give, then I must make an over-all rating of the six. To do this I must in some way combine all the information I have about each student into an index. At another time we may be more interested in how each of several dimensions is related to outside variables. But, even so, we must find a way of combining the indicators, since by their nature the indicators are many, and their relations to outside variables are usually both weaker and more unstable than the underlying characteristic which we would like to measure.

To put it in more formal language, each individual indicator has only a probability relation to what we really want to know. A man might maintain his basic position, but by chance shift on an individual indicator; or he might change his basic position, but by chance remain stable on a specific indicator. But if we have many such indicators in an index, it is highly unlikely that a large number of them will all change in one direction, if the man we are studying has in fact not changed his basic position.

To put the matter in another way, we need a lot of probings if we want to know what a man can really do or where he really stands. This, however, creates great difficulties in the fourth step of the measurement sequence which we described above. If we have many indicators and not all of them move in the same direction, how do we put them together in one index? Only recently have we raised the question: can you really develop a theory to put a variety of indicators together? The subject is a large one, and it is impossible to go into details here. The aim always is to study how these indicators are interrelated with each other, and to derive from these interrelations some general mathematical ideas of what one might call the power of one indicator, as compared with another, to contribute to the specific measurement one wants to make.

In the formation of indices of broad social and psychological concepts, we typically select a relatively small number of items from a large number of possible ones suggested by the concept and its attendant imagery. It is one of the notable features of such indices that their correlation with outside variables will usually be about the same, regardless of the specific "sampling" of items which goes into them from the broader group associated with the concept. This rather startling phenomenon has been labeled "the interchangeability of indices."

II. THE INTERCHANGEABILITY OF INDICES

To present an example, we chose an index of "conservatism" used in a recent study of the response of college teachers of social sciences to the difficult years of the "McCarthy period," with its frequent attacks against colleges and professors for "leftist leanings."

One of our problems in this Teacher Apprehension study was to sort out those teachers who, because of their own convictions, could not possibly be the objects of such attacks: the men and women who hereafter, using the favorite term of their own spokesmen, will be called the conservatives.

From the beginning of our study we sought to find an acceptable way to locate this conservative group correctly. How was that to be done in a relatively short interview, in which the bulk of the questions necessarily was concerned with the nonconservatives who were the ones mainly involved in the controversies? This is a problem of classification common to all survey research. What indicators should we select?

In our study we could have submitted to our respondents certain conservative writings and asked them whether they approved of them. Or we could have selected the organizations they belonged to or the magazines they read as indicators. We preferred, as a result of much previous experience, to choose indicators more closely connected with the rest of the interview. We submitted to each respondent a series of rights and prohibitions, most of them taken from academic life, and asked whether they were for or against them. Out of this material an index of conservatism was formed. Since we were aware that quite different material would have been equally suitable, we tested our index against a series of other possibilities.

Two questions had to do with the respondent's attitude towards student activities. "If there are students who want to join it, do you think that a Young Socialist League ought to be allowed on this campus, or not?" The attitude toward socialists seemed a good indicator because whether they should be classified with communists or not is an issue on which educated conservatives and their opponents are likely to disagree. Fourteen per cent, or 355 professors, reported they would be definitely against such a policy. Characteristically enough, the second question, also pertaining to student activities, gave almost the same number of conservative replies. We asked our respondents to suppose that they were faculty advisers to a student organization on the campus that "proposed inviting Owen Lattimore, Far Eastern expert (now under indictment in Washington) to speak at a public meeting here." Again, about 14 per cent of the sample, in this case 342 professors, put themselves on record that this "ought not to be allowed."

To both questions we get practically the same number of conservative answers: 342 and 355, respectively. One might expect that practically the same professors furnish these replies. This, however, is not completely the case. Table 1 shows how the answers are related.

TABLE 1

A Cross-Tabulation of Answers to the Two Questions on What Students Should Be Permitted To Do

| | Invite Lattimore | | | |
Form a Socialist Club	Approved	Undecided	Disapproved	Total
Approved	1686	95	124	1905
Undecided	118	27	46	191
Disapproved	152	31	172	355
Total	1956	153	342	2451

We see that the great statistical similarity of replies to each question is really the result of a considerable amount of "turnover." Of the people who approved of a Socialist Club, 124 would be against an invitation to Lattimore; conversely, 152 people who approved this invitation would not want students to form a Young Socialist League. This is neither surprising nor disturbing. Any single indicator has a specific element and can never be taken as fully representative for the classification we are striving to achieve—here, the classification of conservative respondents. Many of the interviewees make qualitative comments on their answers, and they do it most often when they see that on a specific point their response is somewhat out of line with their whole attitude pattern. We know, therefore, fairly well what explains the position of the people in the right upper and left lower corners of Table 1. Some of the respondents who were against inviting Lattimore dislike him personally. Others feel that a legal matter is at issue—a man who is under indictment should not be permitted to talk on a college campus. Inversely, the professors who would let Lattimore talk but who are against a Young Socialist League sometimes comment that on their campus there is a general policy against political student organizations or that they feel that a socialist organization could be especially open to subversive infiltration.

Suppose we decided to use one of the items in Table 1 as a crude index to conservatism. A serious discussion could start over which of the two questionnaire items is a better "measure" of conservatism. The Lattimore question is tinged with personal idiosyncrasies and legal implications. The Socialist League item has an element of ambiguity: do those who would forbid such an organization express their own opinion or the policy of their college? Neither of the two items is a very pure "measure," and arguments could therefore continue for and against each of them. Actually, however, it would make very little difference which one is used. And this is a point which needs to be driven home. Classifications in social research are mainly used to establish relations between a number of variables. The crucial question, therefore, is whether these relations, the empirical findings we are looking for, are much affected if we interchange one reasonable index with another.

To exemplify the matter we need an "outside variable." For it we chose the answer to an item which forced the respondent to make a hypothetical choice between the rights of the individual and the claims of the institution:

If you had to make a choice, in a case in which a member of the faculty is accused of being subversive or of engaging in un-American activities, which do you think is *more* important for the college (university) administration to protect—the reputation of the college (university) or the rights of the faculty members?

What is the relation of conservatism to the concern for individual rights? This concern is the outside variable which we want to relate to conservatism. For the latter we have two measures available. Each of them can be tabulated against the choice between the protection of individual rights or the reputation of the college. What difference is there in the choice between the two indicators, namely the Lattimore or the Socialist League item?

The essential fact is that we get practically the same result irrespective of which of the two indicators we use to separate the conservative respondents from the others (Table 2).

TABLE 2

Proportion Giving Priority to Faculty Rights Related to Two Measures of "Conservatism"

Attitude on Lattimore Speech	% Giving Priority to Faculty Rights	Attitude on Socialist League	% Giving Priority to Faculty Rights
Conservative	46%	Conservative	43%
Neutral	50%	Neutral	51%
Permissive	70%	Permissive	70%

Among the "conservatives" to be found in the first line of either column less than half would feel that the faculty rights are paramount. Among the "permissives" in the bottom line more than two-thirds feel this way. The whole numerical trend in the two columns is about the same irrespective of which indicator has been used for classificatory purposes.

In actual research practice, a larger number of items rather than one item alone is used for the purpose of classification. This has a variety of reasons. For example, indices based on more items permit finer distinctions, and they tend to cancel out the peculiarities of any single item. These are details which need not be elaborated here. Even if we use several items for classificatory purposes, we have always a selection out of a much larger pool of reasonable possibilities.

This, then, is the general rule based on very diversified research practice. If we are dealing with a rather broad concept like conservatism, and if we want to "translate" it into an empirical research instrument, a large number of indicators will always be eligible to form an index for classificatory purposes. Only a relatively small number of such items is practically manageable in most field research situations. If we choose two sets of such reasonable items to form two alternative indices, the following two facts will usually be found:

a. The two indices will be related, but they will not classify all the people in a study in precisely the same way; Table 1 exemplifies this.

b. The two indices will usually lead to very similar empirical results if they are cross-tabulated against a third outside variable; Table 2 exemplifies this.

One pays a serious but unavoidable price for the practical advantages of the interchangeability of indices. We can never reach "pure" classifications. Whatever index we use, the items will have "peculiarities" which result in some cases being misclassified, and therefore the empirical relationships which we find are lower than they would be if we had more precise measures of the variables with which the study is concerned.

The tentative character of the rule should also be stressed. There are some variables which are of great and general significance, and therefore over the years ever better instruments have been developed. Intelligence tests, for example, use a very large number of carefully selected items. If we were to use two such tests to classify the same group of people, the number of contradictions would be much smaller than that found in our Table 1. If a long series of studies over many years were intended to see whether the number of conservatives in the population increases, or how conservatism is related to a great many other variables, it would be worthwhile to develop a very refined classification device. But in a study like that of Teacher Apprehension, where a large number of variables had to be introduced for the first time, the only practical course for the researcher is to use fairly simple indices, and to make sure that he does not deceive himself or his readers about the remaining uncertainties.

III. ON THE RELATION BETWEEN INDIVIDUAL AND COLLECTIVE PROPERTIES

Social scientists often make use of variables to describe not only individual persons, but also groups, communities, or other "collectives." Thus, one reads of "racially mixed census tracts," of "highly bureaucratized voluntary organizations," or of a "centrally located rooming house district." At other times the variables, although describing individuals, are based on data about some collectives, as in a comparison of "graduates of top-ranking medical schools" with "graduates of other medical schools." I shall try to clarify some of the operations involved in the construction and use of such variables in empirical research, and to provide a nomenclature for the different ways in which information about individuals and about collectives may be interwoven in these variables.

1. *Some features of generalizing propositions.* Because the intended meaning of such variables often remains ambiguous if they are not examined in the context of certain kinds of propositions in which they are used, it is necessary at the outset to highlight certain features of these propositions:

a. They say something about a set of *elements* ("cases," "units of observation").

b. For the research purposes at hand, these elements are considered comparable. This means that the same set of *properties* is used to describe each of the elements.

c. Each element has a certain value on each property (these values may be quantitative or qualitative).

d. The *propositions* assert interrelationships between the properties.

These features are, of course, common to all empirical or hypothetical generalizations. The propositions with which we are here concerned have the additional characteristic that their elements either are collectives, or are described by reference to collectives. Typical examples of the first case are these: the lower the average income in a precinct, the higher the proportion of Democratic votes cast in a presidential election; tank platoons composed of friends perform better than those composed otherwise. The precinct or the platoon are the elements of these propositions. The properties they relate are average income and voting rate in one example, and some measure of social relation and performance ratings by observers in the other.

2. *Special meaning of "collective" and "member."* The term "collective" is used here in a specific sense which needs clarification. A collective is any element in a proposition composed of *members*, i.e., constituent parts, which are regarded as comparable.

A Boy Scout troop, for example, is a collective, and the Boy Scouts who belong to it are its members. In the same sense, a city can be treated as a collective, with the inhabitants as members. However, the members of a collective are not necessarily individual persons. A city, for example, can be described not only as a collective with the inhabitants as members, but also as a collective with the voting precincts as members. It follows that what appears as a collective in one context (e.g., precincts), can appear as a member in another. But a city could also be introduced as a collective of buildings. In any analysis of a piece of writing in which some of the elements in a proposition are collectives, it is always necessary to specify clearly of what members the collectives are composed (for the purposes at hand).

In some studies, more than two levels appear; for example, inhabitants, precincts, and cities may all be elements of the same study. This whole matter could, therefore, be elaborated by pointing out the various relationships which can exist between inhabitants, precincts, and cities. In the next few pages we restrict ourselves to collectives which have only one kind of members; the members in most illustrations will be individual persons, but we will also present some cases in which the members themselves are larger units (e.g., "communities" considered as members of a state).

3. *Properties of collectives.* It is often useful to distinguish three types of properties which describe collectives: analytical properties based on data about each member; structural properties based on data about the relations among members; and global properties, not based on information about the properties of individual members. The following examples may clarify these distinctions:

a. Analytical properties. These are properties of collectives which are obtained by performing some mathematical operation upon some property of each single member.

The average income in a city is an example of an analytical property of a collective (city) made up of individuals. Another example of an analytical property is the proportion of the communities of a given state that have their own high school; this is a property of a collective (state) the members of which are communities.

The standard deviation of incomes in a nation appears as an analytical property in the following proposition: when incomes in a nation are more equally distributed, people will save more, because they will spend less money on display consumption which might help them be socially acceptable in the higher strata.

Correlations are sometimes used to characterize collectives, and then also constitute analytical properties. The individual correlation of age and prestige in a given community, for example, has been used as a measure of its norms regarding old age. Sometimes more indirect inferences are involved. For example, in urban areas voting is highly correlated with occupation, while this is not the case in rural districts. One may conclude from this that in rural districts there is a stronger spirit of community and cohesion.

b. Structural properties. These are properties of collectives which are obtained by performing some operation on data about the relations of each member to some or all of the others.

Assume for example, that a sociometrist has recorded the "best-liked classmate" of each student in a number of classes. He can then classify the classes according to the degree to which all choices are concentrated upon a few "stars." Or he might, alternately, classify them according to their cliquishness, the latter being defined as the number of subgroups into which a class can be divided so that no choices cut across subgroup lines. In these examples the collective is the class, and the members are the individual students; "concentration of choices" and "cliquishness" are structural properties of the classes.

For an example in which the members are larger units, consider a map of the precincts of a city, which indicates the number of Negroes residing in each. Let a "Negro enclave" be defined as a precinct in which some Negroes live, but which is completely surrounded by precincts without Negroes. The proportion of the precincts of a city which are Negro enclaves would then be a structural property of the city.

c. Global properties. Often collectives are characterized by properties which are not based on information about the properties of individual members.

Nations, for example, may be characterized by the ratio of the national budget alloted to education and to armaments. Army units may be characterized by the cleanliness of their mess equipment. American Indian tribes may be characterized by the frequency with which themes of "achievement motive" make their appearance in their folk tales.

The cultural level of a city might be measured by the presence or absence of certain "cultural" institutions (theatres, libraries, etc.)

or by the proportion of its buildings which are used for cultural purposes.

Having a city manager form of government is a global property of a city. The insistence on specified initiation rites as a prerequisite to membership is a global property of a religious cult or of a college fraternity. Accessibility from the nearest traffic artery is a global property of a village.

"Emergent," "integral," "syntalic" and other terms have been used in meanings very similar to that of our term "global." It is by no means certain which term is most useful, nor have all the logical problems been resolved. Thus, the number of members of a collective (population size, etc.) is classified here as a global property, although one might argue that it is an analytic property, obtained by the operation of counting performed upon the individual property of "existence." Even more ambiguous is the classification of rates based on the behavior of members, e.g., suicide rates.

4. *A subsidiary distinction among analytical properties of collectives.* An interesting distinction may be made among the analytical properties. The first two examples given above were the average income of a city and the proportion of the communities of a given state that have their own high school. These properties of collectives have what one might call a psychological similarity to the properties of members on which they are based. The wealth of a city seems to be the same sort of thing as the wealth of an inhabitant. The endowment of a community with a high school and the proportion of high-school-endowed communities in a state have a parallel meaning.

This is not true for the remaining examples of analytical properties given above—the standard deviation of incomes in a nation, or correlations like that between age and prestige in a given community. Correlations and standard deviations can apply only to collectives and have no parallel on the level of members. The standard deviation of incomes in a city, for example, denotes something quite different— lack of homogeneity, perhaps—from individual income, the datum from which it is computed. Some economists have surmised that the average proportion of income saved in a group is smaller the higher the dispersion of income; a lack of homogeneity supposedly makes for more consumption expenditures at the service of status striving. Average rate of saving in a group is "similar" to individual saving; but homogeneity of income has no "parallel" on the individual level, at least at one point of time. One might speak of a "genuine" analytical variable in the latter case, although the distinction is of a somewhat intuitive nature.

Another variable of this sort is "degree of consensus." When a Democrat and a Republican are competing for the mayoralty, the degree of political consensus in a particular club might be measured by the extent of the club's deviation from a 50-50 split. In this instance the analytic property is measured by a proportion, but it is not the simple proportion of adherents of either party; clubs which are 80 per cent Democratic and those which are 20 per cent Democratic are regarded as equal in consensus.

5. *Properties of individual members of collectives.* Propositions in which the elements are individuals make up the main stock of empirical research findings: rich people vote more Republican, women read more fiction, etc. When people are considered as members of a collective, then their properties can be classified according to whether the rest of the collective enters into the characterization of its members or not. This leads to a classification which to a certain extent corresponds to the one just discussed.

a. Absolute properties. These are characteristics of members which are obtained without making any use either of information about the characteristics of the collective, or of information about the relationships of the member being described to other members. Thus in the preceding examples income and sex were absolute properties.

b. Relational properties. These properties of members are computed from information about the substantive relationships between the member described and other members.

Sociometric popularity-isolation (member of choices received) is a relational property. Many other sociometric indices fall into this category. For example, if each member of a small group has rated each other member on a 5-point scale of acceptance-rejection, each member can be characterized by the total score he received (popularity), by the total score he expressed (active sociability), by the average deviation of the scores he accorded the others (discrimination in his acceptance of other members), etc. In a study of the diffusion of the use of a new drug through a community of doctors, the physicians were classified according to whether or not they had a friend who had already used the new drug on a certain date.

c. Comparative properties. These characterize a member by a comparison between his value on some (absolute or relational) property with the distribution of this property over the entire collective of which he is a member.

Sibling order is a comparative property of individuals in the proposition, "First-born children are more often maladjusted than intermediate and last-born children." Note that each individual is characterized by comparison with the age of the other individuals in his family; in the resulting classification, many of the "last-born" will be older in years than many of the "first-born."

Another example is contained in the following proposition: "Students who had the highest I.Q. in their respective high school classes have greater difficulty in adjusting in college than students who were not quite at the top in high school, even when their actual I.Q. score is equally high." Here the comparative property (being at the top in high school or not) is established in terms of the I.Q. distribution in each student's respective high school; the proposition pertains to a set of college students which includes boys from several high schools (collectives).

d. Contextual properties. These describe a member by a property of his collective.

Consider the example: "Graduates of large law schools are more likely to earn high incomes at age 40 than graduates of small law schools." In this proposition, "being a member of a large law school" is a contextual property of individuals.

Contextual properties are also used in the following propositions: "Union members in closed shops are less militant than union members in open shops." "Residents of racially mixed districts show more racial prejudice than those of racially homogeneous districts." "Soldiers in units where many promotions have been granted are less satisfied with the promotion policy than those in units where few promotions have been granted." In these propositions, being a member of a closed shop, residing in a mixed district, or being a soldier in a unit with frequent promotions are all examples of contextual properties.*

---

* The contextual properties can of course be divided once more according to the distinctions made in the previous section. Observe the difference between the poor man raised in a neighborhood "where everyone else was rich" and the American lawyer who was trained in a country "where Roman law pre-

Note that a contextual property, unlike a comparative property, has the same value for all members of a given collective. It is not meaningful to speak of contextual or comparative properties when the elements under study are all members of the same collective, for instance, when only graduates of one law school are being studied. The reason is that any *contextual* property would, in that case, have the same value for all the elements; hence nothing could be said about the interrelationship of this property to any other property. Any *comparative* property would, under these circumstances, classify the elements in exactly the same way as the absolute property from which it was derived, except that the calibration may be grosser.

An interesting situation comes about as follows. We have a set of collectives, and take as elements of a proposition all their members (or a representative sample of the members of each); one property of the proposition is a contextual one. Suppose, for instance, we take all the graduates of fifty law schools in the United States as of a certain year, and see how large their income is ten years later. The resultant finding may be "the income of law school graduates is correlated with the size of the school they graduated from;" this is a proposition about students, relating their income (an absolute property) to the size of their law school (a contextual property). The same proposition could be interpreted also as one where the elements are the law schools: the average income of the students would then be an analytical property of each law school; its size would be a global property of these collectives.

At first sight one may feel that the distinctions made in this section are not much more than an exercise in elementary logic. Actually they have a bearing on major discussions which have continued for years. In the debate between Durkheim and Tarde, for instance, the former waved the flag of the "social fact" against his opponent the psychologist. The issue, properly formulated, is whether a system of propositions can be built up, the elements of which are exclusively collectives. Durkheim would not have insisted on using only global

---

vailed." It seems not worthwhile to follow these combinations into further detail. It is, however, useful to emphasize the difference between a relational characteristic of a member and a contextual characteristic based on a structural property of the collective. An example of the former would be the sociometric isolate; an example of the latter would be a man who comes from an atomized group (containing many isolates, irrespective of whether he is an isolate himself or not).

characteristics, such as tribal customs or laws; his notion of density of contact is a structural, and the suicide rate conceivably an analytical, property of a collective. The real issue is whether it is necessary to introduce propositions the elements of which are individuals in order to develop a coherent system of social theory. A radical Durkheim position denying this necessity is today rather unlikely.

Another controversy can be clarified with the help of the preceding analysis. The objection is often raised that social research is atomistic and therefore does not take into account the complexities of social reality. This is sometimes put into the form that "wholes" or "structures" cannot be described by combinations of "separate" variables. Using the word structure in this general sense we can see that its meaning is caught in the following two ways:

a. by propositions in which the elements are collectives, if the latter are characterized by structural properties in the narrow sense of the preceding pages;

b. by propositions in which the elements are individuals, if the latter are partly characterized by contextual properties.

This case is important enough to deserve a special example provided by a study of college students. Norman Miller has analyzed tests measuring attitudes toward labor. He showed that students who came from a middle class background (a contextual property) became relatively more anti-labor between Freshman and Senior year while students from labor background became progressively more pro-labor. The correlation between age and attitude is different according to the background of the students.

The main finding in this last example is due to combining more than two variables into a proposition. What can we say in general about this procedure of multi-variable analysis?

IV. THE ANALYSIS OF STATISTICAL RELATIONS

In the preceding sections we have referred to many relations between two variables. For our present purpose we can assume that they were all dichotomous attributes and that we are interested in one question only: are the two attributes related or not? For our answer we have to form a cross-tabulation of the following form:

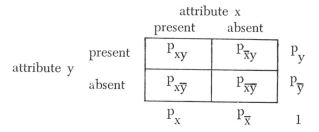

The symbolism is simple: $p_{\bar{x}y}$ for instance is the proportion of people who are y but not x. If x and y are unrelated then

$$\frac{p_{xy}}{p_{\bar{x}y}} = \frac{p_{x\bar{y}}}{p_{\bar{x}\bar{y}}}$$

This means that the presence of x is relatively equally frequent among those people who are and those who are not y. The preceding condition can be expressed in terms of the so-called *crossproduct*

$$[xy] = p_{xy}\, p_{\bar{x}\bar{y}} - p_{\bar{x}y}\, p_{x\bar{y}}.$$

If $[xy] = 0$ (vanishes) then x and y are unrelated. (Sampling problems are not relevant in the present context.)

Now suppose that a third attribute t is introduced. Then we can develop the two correlative operations of *mixture* and of *elaboration*. A numerical example of mixture is given in the following scheme:

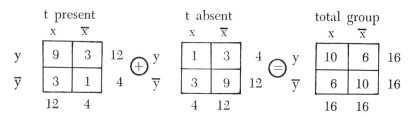

In the two tables on the left the variables x and y are unrelated. But if we mix the two groups originally separated according to t we do find that people who are y are also more likely to be x than those who are not y.

Elaboration is mixture in reverse order. It consists in decomposing the group on the right into two subgroups and studying the relation of x and y separately for people who are and are not t. Elaboration is clearly not a unique operation. We could obtain the right side, e.g., by mixing the two following subgroups:

	t present					t absent					total group		
	x	$\bar{x}$				x	$\bar{x}$				x	$\bar{x}$	
y	5	3	8	$\oplus$	y	5	3	8	$\ominus$	y	10	6	16
$\bar{y}$	3	5	8		$\bar{y}$	3	5	8		$\bar{y}$	6	10	16
	8	8				8	8				16	16	

There is one important difference between this and the preceding scheme. Both attributes x and y were formerly related to t. Neither *[xt]* nor *[yt]* were zero. In the new scheme we find that the proportion of x and y is the same for people who are and are not *t:*

$$[xt] = 0 \text{ and } [yt] = 0.$$

We shall call the relations on the left side of the schemes *partial relations* (depending on t) and symbolize them by *[xy;t]* and *[xy;t̄]* respectively. Elaboration then consists of studying how *[xy]* depends upon *[xy;t]* and *[xy;t̄]* under varying conditions of *[xt]* and *[yt]*. An algebraic development of the problems leads to the general formula.

Formula (1):

$$[xy] = \frac{[xy;t]}{P_t} + \frac{[xy;\bar{t}]}{P_{\bar{t}}} + \frac{[xt] \cdot [ty]}{P_t \cdot P_{\bar{t}}}.$$

The original relationship can be described as the sum of the two partial relationships and an additional factor, which is the product of what are called the marginal relationships between the test factor and each of the two original variables.

This elaboration leads to two major forms. Either the two partial relations may vanish; then formula (1) reduces to

Formula (2a):

$$[xy] = \frac{[xt] \cdot [ty]}{P_t \cdot P_{\bar{t}}}.$$

Or the test factor t might be unrelated to x (this means that *[xt]* = 0), and we then have

Formula (2b):

$$[xy] = \frac{[xy;t]}{P_t} + \frac{[xy;\bar{t}]}{P_{\bar{t}}},$$

a form which will turn out of interest only if one of these two partial relations is markedly stronger than the other. We shall call this the P-form (emphasis on partials), while formula (2a) will be called the M-form (emphasis on what the statistician calls "marginals").

To this formal distinction we now add a substantive one: the time order of the 3 variables. Assuming that x is prior to y, then t either can be located between x and y in time, or it can precede both. In the former case we talk of an intervening test variable, in the latter case of an antecedent one. We thus have 4 major possibilities.

	Statistical Form	
	P	M
Position of t		
Antecedent	PA	MA
Intervening	PI	MI

We are now ready to present the decisive point. It is claimed that there are essentially four operations which can be performed with two original and one test variable. It makes no difference whether this is done with actual data or whether they take the form of theoretical analyses. If a relation between two variables is analyzed in the light of a third, only these four operations or combinations thereof will occur irrespective of whether they are called interpretation, understanding, theory, or anything else.

We now turn to some concrete examples which will clarify what these four types of elaboration stand for. In cases of the type PA, we usually call the test variable t a "condition." General examples easily come to mind, although in practice they are fairly rare and are a great joy to the research man when they are found. For example, the propaganda effect of a film is greater among less-educated than among highly educated people. The depression had worse effects on authoritarian families than on other types.

Three general remarks can be made about this type of finding or reasoning: (a) It corresponds to the usual stimulus-disposition-response sequence, with x being the stimulus and the antecedent t being the disposition. (b) The whole type might best be called one of *specification*. One of the two partials will necessarily be larger than the original relationship. We specify, so to speak, the circumstances under which the original relationship holds true more strongly. (c) Usually we will go on from there and ask why the relationship is stronger on one side of the test dichotomy. This might then lead into one of the other types of analysis. Durkheim uses types PA in discussing why married people commit suicide less than unmarried people. He introduces as a test variable "a nervous tendency to suicide, which the family, by its influence, neutralizes or keeps from developing." This is type PA exactly. We do not take it to be a convincing explanation because the introduction of the hypothetical test variable (tendency to suicide) sounds rather tautological. We rather want to know why the family keeps this tendency from developing, which leads to type MI, as we shall see later.

The type PI is also easily exemplified. We study the relationship between job success *(y)* and whether children did or did not go to progressive schools *(x)*. We find that if the progressively educated children come into an authoritarian job situation *(t)* they do less well in their work than the others; on the other hand, if they come into a democratic atmosphere, their job success is greater.

The relation between type of education and job success is elaborated by an intervening test factor, the work atmosphere. We call such a test factor a "contingency." In many prediction studies, the predicted value depends upon subsequent circumstances which are not related to the predictor. An example is the relation between occupational status and participation in the life of a housing community. White-collar people participate more if they are dissatisfied, whereas manual workers participate more if they are satisfied with their jobs.

Type MA is used mainly when we talk of rectifying what is usually called a *spurious relationship*. It has been found that the more fire engines that come to a fire *(x)*, the larger is the damage *(y)*. Because fire engines are used to reduce damage, the relationship is startling and requires elaboration. As a test factor *(t)* the size of the fire is introduced. The partials then become zero and the original result appears as the product of two marginal relationships; the larger the fire, the more engines—and also the more damage.

When we encounter a relationship which is psychologically puzzling, we usually stop at that point; but this same mode of elaboration is also used under different psychological circumstances. More people commit suicide during the summer than during the winter. Durkheim suggests, as a *t* factor for elaboration, that increased social activities are going on during the summer. Our general knowledge tells us that *x* (the season) is indeed related to *t* in this way.

Our interest immediately shifts to the *[ty]* relationship, namely: the presumed fact that greater intensity of social life leads to more suicides. Actually, of course, whether this explanation which comes from Durkheim is correct would depend upon a disappearance of the partials. Durkheim would have to show that if intensity of social life is kept constant, the season does not make any difference in suicides. Because he has no data on this point, he looks for other situations where he can presume the intensity of social life to vary. He finds that there are more suicides during the day as compared with the number during the night, which he again explains with the help of the same test factor. This leads into the whole question of probability of inference, which we do not follow up here.

We now turn to type MI, for which we shall use the term *"interpretation."* The difference between "explanation" and "interpretation" in this context is related to the time sequence between *x* and *t*. In an interpretation, *t* is an intervening variable situated between *x* and *y* in the time sequence.

Examples of type MI are numerous. Living in a rural community rather than a city *(x)* is related to a lower suicide rate *(y)*. The greater intimacy of rural life *(t)* is introduced as an intervening variable. If we had a good test of cohesion, we should undoubtedly find that a community being a rural rather than an urban one *(x)* is positively correlated with its degree of cohesion *(t)*, and that greater cohesion *(t)* is correlated with lower suicide rates *(y)*. But obviously some rural communities will have less cohesion than some urban communities. If cohesion is kept constant as a statistical device, then the partial relationship between the rural-urban variable and the suicide rate would have to disappear.

It might be useful to illustrate the difference between type MA and type MI in one more example. It was found during the war that married women working in factories had a higher rate of absence from work than single women. Here are a number of possible elaborations:

a. Test factor: more responsibilities at home. This is an intervening variable. If it is introduced and the two partial relationships—

between marital status and absenteeism—disappear, we have an elaboration of type MI. We interpret the relation by showing what intervening variable connects the original two variables.

b. Test factor: physical infirmity as crudely measured by age; the *older* women are more likely to be married, and to have less physical strength, both as a result of their age. Age is an antecedent variable. If it turns out, when age is kept constant, that the relation between marital status and absenteeism disappears, we would have an explanation, and probably call it a spurious effect: type MA.

The latter case suggests again an important point. After having explained the original relationship, our attention might shift to *[ty]*, the fact that older people show a higher absentee rate. This, in turn, might lead to new elaborations: is it really the case that older women have less physical resistance, be they married or single? Or, is it that older women have been born in a time when work is not as yet important for women and, therefore, they have a lower work morale. In other words, after one elaboration is completed, we will, as good scientists, immediately turn to a new one; but the basic analytical processes will always be the same.

One final point can be cleared up, at least to a certain degree, by this analysis. We can suggest a clear-cut definition of the *causal* relation between two attributes. If we have a relationship between x and y, and if for any *antecedent* test factor the partial relationships between x and y do not disappear, then the original relationship should be called a causal one. It makes no difference here whether the necessary operations are actually carried through or made plausible by general reasoning. In a controlled experiment we have two matched groups: the experimental exposure corresponds to the variable x, and the observed effect to y. Matching makes sure that for any antecedent t we shall have $[xt] = 0$. If then $[xy] \neq 0$ we can in the light of the preceding analysis always be sure that there is a causal relation between exposure x and effect y.

This has special bearing on the following kind of discussion. It is found that in densely populated areas the crime rate is higher than in sparsely populated areas. Some authors state that this could not be considered a true causal relationship, but such a remark is often used in two very different ways. Assume an intervening variable, for instance, the increased irritation which is the result of crowded conditions. Such an interpretation does not detract from the causal character of the original relationship. On the other hand, the argument might go this way: crowded areas have cheaper rents and, therefore, attract poorer, partly demoralized people. Here the character of the inhabitants is antecedent to the characteristics of the area. In this case the original relationship is indeed explained as a spurious one and should not be called causal.

We can, finally, link the present discussion with some observations made in the previous section. Explanation consists of the formal aspect of elaboration and some substantive ordering of variables. We have here focused on ordering by time sequence. But not all variables can be ordered this way. We saw that we can distinguish orders of complexity, e.g., variables characterizing persons, collectives, and sets of collectives. Other ordering principles could be introduced, e.g., degree of generality, exemplified by the instance of a specific opinion, a broader attitude, and a basic value system. What is needed is to combine the formalism of elaboration with a classification of variables according to different ordering principles. This would cover a great part of what needs to be known about the logic of explanation and inference in contemporary survey analysis.

V. MATHEMATICAL MODELS—SOME USES AND LIMITATIONS

So far, we have discussed how observations are organized into concepts and indices, and how relationships among several variables are analyzed. There is, however, a small group of social scientists which tries to go even further and builds mathematical models of human behavior.

It is useful to divide the area of models into what we may call 1) static or measurement models, and 2) dynamic or behavioral models. Anyone who develops a theory of scaling works in a static area. That is to say, he relates manifest data to underlying utility or probability. One who deals, let us say, with learning theory, or with the kind of work which Rashevsky does, where the element of time enters, works in the second field. There is, of course, some overlapping. For example, the problem of introducing scales and measurements in dynamic models is very important. One of the main reasons for the criticisms of Rashevsky is that he uses dynamic models that introduce characteristics of people without concerning himself about the measurement of the characteristics. But it is worth while to remember that most of our normal work conveniently divides into those models which are used to develop variables, such as attitudes, utility, or scales, and those models which are used to analyze dynamic behavior, such as learning or changes in social systems.

Most of these remarks will deal with the second type, the dynamic models, because of their relevance to problems which interest the majority of non-mathematical sociologists. They are not interested in the formation of units or scales; they take that for granted. They call in "George" to do it, and they believe in his technical ability. But after George has developed a "scale," what they want to know is how it can be used for the analysis of social processes.

There are two major problems in this area on which we need greater clarification:

1) What are the scientific tasks which mathematical models can perform in the broad area of social science?

2) How is the choice of the specific area in which we develop models made?

As to the uses of models, there is no doubt that one important function is to help predict behavior. But there is another function which might be called the *linguistic* function of models in the social sciences. There may be a great value in developing models on their own merits, irrespective of whether we have any data or of whether they can at this moment predict anything at all.

The crux is, of course, the meaning of the term "data." Experiments might be the only source of data for the physicist, and they might be useful for the social scientist, but they are for us certainly not the main material we are working with today. We have data which have been accumulating for about 2,500 years. Plato developed very interesting propositions on human behavior in society, and if we now developed models which somehow organized or clarified what Plato had to say, we should be doing an important job.

Some interesting illustrations of the linguistic function of mathematical models could be drawn from efforts to "translate" humanistic writings. However, here we shall draw our examples from recent empirical studies, and show that even in this area there is an important task of clarification which does not involve prediction.

The linguistic function of mathematical models can be divided into three parts: 1) the organizing function, 2) the analytical function, and 3) the mediating function.

As an example of the *organizing function,* consider the many studies which are now available on how people vote and why they vote. One finding which has been well corroborated in different studies is that Catholics for many decades in this country have been voting much more frequently Democratic than have Protestants. A number of recent studies refined this result. We made studies during election campaigns, interviewing people every month, asking them how they intended to vote, and classifying voters as Democratic Catholics, Republican Catholics, etc. In August, most Catholics said that they intended to vote Democratic, and most Protestants said that they planned to vote Republican. In October, when the same people were asked the same questions, there were some changes. The Catholic Democrats and the Republican Protestants kept their conviction, but the other two groups showed changes. Republican Catholics started to say, "I changed my mind; I think I had better vote Democratic." And many of the Protestants who had wanted to vote Democratic began to change their minds and veer to the Republicans. This is true not only for Catholics and Protestants, but for urban and rural groups as well; urban dwellers are more likely to be Democrats. This leads to a generalization on a somewhat higher level. People who want to vote in agreement with their own group are much more likely to be stable in their intention than the people who intend to vote against the prevailing trend of their group. As time goes on, the people who first want to vote against the prevailing trend in their group slowly "return to the fold."

Offhand it would seem easy to understand this by referring to the influence of the environment. And indeed we have information that people with similar social characteristics are more likely to meet one another, and that such contacts affect the vote intention of the participants. But why does the population not split into groups which are homogeneous within and completely different from each other? Obviously there are countertrends, and one of them is the random fluctuation of people who have little interest in politics. This uninterested group is larger between elections than during campaigns and guarantees a certain amount of reshuffling. At the same time the uninterested people introduce another complication. They are less likely to talk politics, but are more easily influenced when they do.

One could go on enumerating the many well-established but disconnected propositions relating attitude, social characteristics, contact frequencies, etc. But no one knows what the minimum of variables and relations are from which the total set could be derived. Here is where the organizing function of mathematics enters. In the small-group field, H. Simon has shown how much clarity can thus be gained. In the area of voting, inventories of propositions have been made, but the final formalization is still lacking.

The *analytical function* of models is exemplified by studies showing that groups appear to solve problems better than individuals. In the election example we have an overabundance of data, and it is a function of the mathematical models to organize them. In the problem-solving case we have a deficiency of data, and the mathematical model points out where we should look further. The notion of group problem-solving is vague. Do we mean a kind of division of labor within the group? Or do we mean that in a group there is a greater probability that one outstanding person will appear and find the answer for all the rest? Empirical studies are available showing the probability of both individual and group solutions. It is then possible to set up two models: one assuming division of labor, and one assuming solution by a top individual in the group. Derivations from the two models can be tested against the data. The model helps us to infer what is going on within the group while it works, although we know only the final outcome. This analytical use of mathematical models often leads to ideas of what new empirical work is needed.

The *mediating function* of model construction can be illustrated as follows. Economists have asserted for eighty years that one cannot measure utilities. Social psychologists have, for the last thirty years, measured attitudes without worrying whether this was a legitimate operation. Perhaps economists did not measure utilities because they spent so much time on the problem of whether utilities could be measured. Only by putting the utility and the attitude problems into a formal language, and thereby showing that they are really the same problem, could there be a joining of effort between the people who have conceptual problems and the people who measured without realizing that the conceptual problem existed. We begin to have now a way of formulating the problem correctly; economists believe it is susceptible to measurement; and social psychologists realize that measurement is not as easy as they thought before.

The mediating function of the formalization appears in a variety of other areas. For instance, almost any textbook in sociology has a final chapter on social change or the lack of it. But the chapters on social change make sense only if one has read a reasonable book on business cycle analysis or economic growth. Sociologists have discussed relations between the individual and society for a hundred and fifty years; physicists have considered the relations between thermodynamics and atomic theory; "aggregation" is a word familiar to economists. When problems are put into formal mathematical language, similarities become obvious—a very important cross-disciplinary mediating function. Only after problems have been formalized is it really possible to work on cross-disciplinary approaches and to make mutual contributions from one discipline to another.

Thus the linguistic function of a mathematical model helps to organize an abundance of material, helps to pin down deficiencies of data, and helps to mediate between procedures that are formally alike but terminologically different—a function of mathematical models which has been often underrated.

Now to the second major point. Are we judicious enough in the choice of the subject matter to which we apply our mathematical efforts? Those who contrive experiments to test mathematical models of human behavior tend to introduce gambling situations. The decision problems social scientists deal with are different: Why do people commit crimes? Why do they buy cars? Why did they vote for Eisenhower? Social scientists in general study decision problems. But when it comes to model construction, mathematicians are interested mainly in how people bet. Perhaps we are again facing a danger which we faced about forty years ago, at the time of the early Watsonian behaviorists. When the idea of learning experiments emerged, there was a general conviction that only in very primitive situations could one really experiment. The main learning effort was concentrated on rats. But social psychologists are more interested in people, and today in America we are no longer convinced that the study of animal psychology can solve the major problems of human psychology.

As mathematical models become important there is a real danger that we repeat the cycle, that we start again at the lowest rung of the ladder. One cannot study how rats bet, but one can study how human beings bet. The relative ease of these experiments seems to me to tempt mathematical model builders to repeat the error of the behavioristic extremists. There are, of course, those who feel that Watson was right. They should at least agree that the concentration of model-building on betting is an analogous situation. The rat maze and the betting experiment are characterized by the same tendency to seek the simplest configuration.

Connected with the choice of area is another choice, that of experiment *versus* observation. I have not been convinced by accounts of the history of psychology that the strong emphasis on experimentation is justified. One can experiment with how people bet. But if one wants to know how people vote, and how people buy, one cannot really experiment. One has to make systematic analytical observations. In the voting studies we have made, we took a sample of people in a small town in New York, and interviewed them every month. We asked them for whom they wanted to vote, and then observed how they changed from month to month. In another study, we kept potential car buyers under observation for nine months, and tried to study the decision process by re-interviewing the same people in various stages of their approach to a final purchase. Somewhat more attention should be devoted to observational data taken over a time interval. The models to be looked for have a similarity to the business cycle analysis of economists. The whole new mathematics of economic growth and population growth are relevant here. In any problem which involves time-series analysis, in any complex problem that involves a comparison of a series of variables over a number of time periods, the relationship of the model to the data is somewhat different from that in the experimental situation.

* * *

THE TOPICS here chosen for review may seem arbitrary, but they have one feature in common: they are entirely characteristic of empirical social science research today. There is a danger that methodological discussions become very general and miss the relevant detail by trying to be all-embracing. In a Colloquium, the theme of which is the unity of the sciences, it is salutary to reverse the old French proverb: the more it is the same, the more one should stress the differences. It is the new step in the over-arching continuity which leads to progress.

BIBLIOGRAPHICAL NOTE

The general theory of index-formation is exemplified in Section I of the *Language of Social Research* edited by P. F. Lazarsfeld and

M. Rosenberg (Free Press, 1955). There one will also find additional material on the interchangeability of indices. An inventory of group properties as used in current sociological literature is provided by R. K. Merton on pages 311-325 of his *Social Theory and Social Structure* (second edition, Free Press, 1957); a good discussion of the general principles involved was given by P. M. Blau in the *American Journal of Sociology* (Volume 63, 1957, p. 58 ff.). Many concrete examples of the treatment of multivariant statistical relations will be found in Chapter VII of H. H. Hyman's *Survey, Design and Analysis* (Free Press, 1955). The organizing use of mathematics is shown at its best in Section 2, H. A. Simon, *Models of Man* (Wiley, 1957). The literature on group problem-solving models is reviewed by I. D. Lorge and H. Solomon in *Psychometrical* (Volume 20, 1955, p. 139 ff.).

In Search of a Poison

Jacob Fine

A few weeks ago a fifty-year-old pawnbroker came to his shop in South Boston at 7:00 A.M. because the police found it had been rifled. At 7:30 A.M., as he leaned over, a loaded pistol fell from his shoulder holster to the floor, and a bullet penetrated his abdomen and came out through his back. All he noticed at the time was a bruise on the skin of his abdomen. He called his physician, saying that he wanted the bruise dressed. The physician asked to speak to the policeman, who was told to bring the man to the hospital. The victim arrived at 8:15 A.M., unconscious and in deep shock; the skin was cold, moist, and very pale, the pulse was fast, already the blood pressure was unobtainable, and there was no urine in the bladder. Transfusions were started immediately, but there was no response, either in blood pressure or otherwise.

The abdomen was opened about 10:30 A.M. Some three liters of blood were sucked out, three small intestinal perforations were sealed, and the lacerated left kidney and spleen were removed. The operation was completed by 2:00 P.M. In addition to the customary therapeutic measures taken after the operation, twenty-three trans-fusions had been given by 7:00 P.M. But the man died that evening without regaining consciousness or recovering a significant blood pressure.

This is an account of shock due to hemorrhage that was *irreversible* in spite of appropriate therapy. A young soldier with such an injury during World War II, or in Korea in 1951, would almost certainly have responded to the treatment given. On replacing the lost blood the skin would have become warm, dry, and pink, the urine would have returned, the pulse would have slowed, and the blood pressure risen to normal. In that case, we would have labeled the shock *reversible*. Hundreds of thousands of comparable injuries occur every year during war and peace. While the great majority of such victims respond to therapy, a disturbing number of them do not, especially those of middle or advanced age. The problem exemplified by the case of the pawnbroker was to discover the mechanism by which the *irreversible* state of shock develops, which causes death in such a short time. The aim of this paper is to set forth a step-by-step account of the search for this mechanism.

Before doing so we should note that the state of irreversible shock can be produced by many types of injury other than hemorrhage. It may also be caused, for example, by an extensive burn, or by a severe pummeling of tissues as by a blast in a mine, or by a fracture of the femur or other large bone, by a fall from a ladder, and so forth. In these forms of trauma there is a combination of tissue injury and loss of blood or blood plasma either to the outside of the body or within the body tissues or spaces. The shock can be severe and irreversible even though the blood loss is not critical. The severest and most rapidly fatal form of shock is that caused by overwhelming infection. In some infections, e.g., in cholera, a critical loss of fluids may occur so rapidly as to produce shock and death within a few hours. In many other infections the fluid loss is relatively minor, and shock then may be due to a sluggish flow of blood, which moves as water does through a swamp.

Regardless of how shock is produced, the fundamental pathology is the same: there is an acute and persisting deficiency of flow of blood through the tissues. This deficiency deprives the tissues of their normal complement of oxygen and a host of other substances provided by the blood, and impedes the removal of waste products. If unrelieved, this situation leads inevitably to failure of some vital function and to death. The time of death depends on how soon any one of the vital functions fails.

Theoretically, it is a simple matter to treat shock precipitated by a critical loss of blood or blood plasma. In most cases the lost blood is replaced as rapidly as possible, the leak is sealed, and shock disappears. But in our search we were concerned with another problem: the instances in which the circulatory apparatus does not respond by a proper distribution of blood *after an existing* deficit has been restored. What explains the failure of the circulatory apparatus to distribute blood properly, either after the lost fluid has been restored or when there has never been a loss of blood volume? Does the integrity of the circulatory apparatus depend upon some organ that has failed to provide its continuously needed protection, or are the vessels themselves impaired so that they can no longer propel the blood along?

We get astonishingly little illumination of this problem from gross or microscopic study of the tissues of the shock victim. Except for tiny localized hemorrhages here and there, especially in the wall of the intestine, there are virtually no signs characteristic of the process. Morbid anatomy is uncommunicative, perhaps because we are dealing with a subtle biochemical disorder. If we examine the behavior of the vital organs during shock, what do we find? Neither the brain nor the lungs seem to be irretrievably damaged, even in the advanced state of shock. The heart is not at fault. It is true that it is not pumping enough blood, but this is because the volume of blood returning to the heart from the veins is far below normal. The kidneys and adrenals are stumbling; but even when they are totally functionless their failure does not kill as rapidly as shock kills.

The only vital organ that remains to be considered is the liver. Could the failure of some function of the liver destroy the host as rapidly as shock can? Removal of the liver from a normal animal results in death in eight to twelve hours. We do not know precisely why. This organ's known functions are numerous, and there are doubtless many yet to be revealed. All the tests of its functional behavior that we can apply show that the liver severely suffers in shock.

Some fifteen years ago several of my collaborators and I began a study of defects in liver function that might contribute to death in shock. We had a suspicion that a biochemical lesion in the liver might somehow impair the capacity of the terminal vessels to propel the blood through the capillaries, and thence into the large veins. We undertook a test of this hypothesis by an experiment designed to prevent such a lesion, and to see if this, in turn, would prevent the circulatory collapse. The plan of the experiment was simple: We would arrange to provide an adequate flow of blood through the liver, while the rest of the circulation remained in a state of shock.

Before describing this experiment, we must describe the control experiment, which is the point of departure for all our subsequent observations: the groin of a dog or rabbit is anesthetized with Novocain. The femoral artery, which is the major artery to the leg, is exposed through a small incision in the groin, and is connected to a bottle containing an anticoagulant (as shown schematically in Fig. 1). The artery is then allowed to bleed freely into the bottle. The bottle is elevated to a height that allows the blood pressure to equilibrate at the lowest level the animal can tolerate (30 mm Hg for the dog,

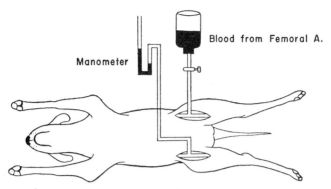

Manometer

Blood from Femoral A.

Fɪɢ. 1.   Schematic representation of the hemorrhagic shock experiment. The animal (dog or rabbit) lies on a table. Novocain is injected and glass tubes are placed in the femoral arteries.   One tube connects to a blood pressure manometer; the other allows blood to enter an elevated flask containing heparin, which prevents the blood from clotting.   The height of the flask is so adjusted that bleeding stops when the blood pressure has fallen to the selected low level (30 mm of mercury in the dog, 50 mm in the rabbit).   The animal is then in deep shock and remains so unless transfused by return of all the blood it lost.

50 mm Hg for the rabbit).   This level of pressure is reached almost immediately after bleeding starts, and it remains there.   The bleeding continues and reaches a maximum within about one hour (see Fig. 2). This maximum is about 53 ml/kg in all mammalian species so far studied.   Within the framework of these two fairly reliable constants, i.e., a fixed level of low blood pressure (hypotension) and a fairly fixed blood volume loss, we then observe that the animal exhibits all the classic features of shock.   It shows the same signs that were observed in the pawnbroker, except for unconsciousness, which is not a classic feature of shock.

If nothing further is now done to the animal, blood begins to return from the bottle to the animal at a variable rate.   This happens because the tone of the blood vessels weakens, resistance is reduced, and the blood pressure tends to fall, thus allowing back-flow from the bottle. We say in physiological terms that the circulation is decompensating, by which we mean that it is becoming unequal to the burden.   If after two hours all the blood still in the bottle is forcibly transfused, then the blood pressure response is good, for it becomes normal and remains so, and the shock rapidly disappears.   Within several hours

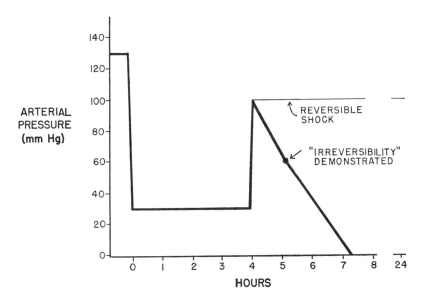

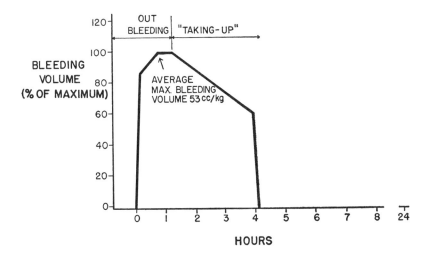

Fig. 2. Arterial pressure (top) and relative volume of blood lost (bottom) by dog in shock.

virtually full function is regained, and sustained recovery follows. *This is the experimental counterpart of reversible hemorrhagic shock in man.*

But if, in the experiment discussed above, nothing is done after two hours—i.e., if the remaining blood in the bottle is allowed to return spontaneously instead of being forcibly transfused—about half of it returns to the animal by the fourth or fifth hour. If at *this* time the remainder in the bottle is forcibly transfused, the blood pressure rises, but falls again soon thereafter; and although the animal no longer has a blood deficit, it nevertheless dies at about the sixth hour or within the next twelve hours. *This is the experimental counterpart of irreversible hemorrhagic shock in man.*

The only difference between the reversible and irreversible types of experimental hemorrhagic shock is the time of exposure to the blood loss. What is happening between the second and the fourth or fifth hours that converts the state of shock that is reversible by transfusion to the state of shock that is not reversible by transfusion? If we can answer this question we should have the key to the cause of death in the animal, and, hopefully, also in man.

We sought for an answer in the injury suffered by the liver. In the liver experiment a dog was put into shock in the manner described. Its portal vein, which is the vessel that carries all the blood from the intestine to the liver, was connected to a large artery of a healthy dog lying at the side of the shocked dog (see Fig. 3). The healthy donor dog's artery was allowed to supply to the shocked dog's liver, via the portal vein, the full complement of blood that the liver normally receives in the healthy state. Balance of flow between the two dogs in this experiment was maintained by returning as much blood from the shocked dog to the donor as the donor was losing to the shocked dog's liver. This cross circulation continued for five hours, at which time the donor dog was disconnected from the recipient. The donor dog was none the worse for wear. The dog in shock was then transfused with all the blood still left in the bottle. The response to this transfusion was full recovery, whereas, without the additional supply of arterial blood to the liver, the dog would have died. Of course, we had previously demonstrated that such perfusion via any other vein did not protect the animal.

This experiment proved that if the liver receives a full supply of normal blood while every other part of the body is in shock, irreversibility to transfusion is prevented. Hence the liver plays a critical

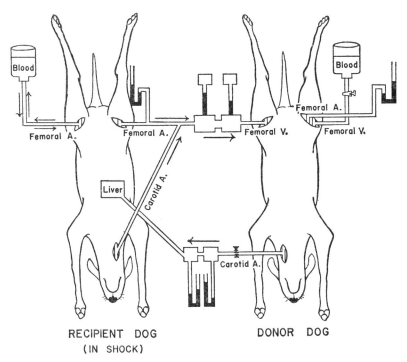

RECIPIENT DOG   DONOR DOG
(IN SHOCK)

Fig. 3.   Schematic representation of cross-circulation of blood between healthy donor dog and dog in shock.

role in the maintenance of vascular integrity. Does the liver in shock lose a substance that it normally provides to sustain the integrity of the blood vessels? Or, since the liver is the most important detoxicating organ in the body, is the ability of the circulation properly to distribute the blood to the tissues permanently destroyed by a poison that develops because of poor flow and that the shocked liver fails to destroy for the same reason?

Our reason for thinking that a toxin might be injuring the circulatory apparatus in hemorrhagic shock is this: the type of shock caused by overwhelming infection is irreparable from the beginning, whether there is a blood volume deficiency or not. We assume that in such a case the irreparable state of the circulation is due to a noxious substance elaborated by bacteria because we know that certain of such products can injure blood vessels. Might such a product also develop in simple hemorrhagic shock, so that eventually the circulation would not respond even after the blood loss was fully restored? Thus we began to look for signs of infection in hemorrhagic shock. Conventional cultural techniques did not provide evidence of the presence of bacteria in the blood and tissues. But failure to find them is not a reliable basis for excluding the presence of bacterial products. Nor did we find the characteristic signs that the body ordinarily displays in developing the defense reactions to bacterial poisons. These reactions require the setting in motion of certain synthetic processes that can be seen in operation in ordinary circumstances, but which the body in shock might not manifest because it might not be able to mobilize the energy reserves needed for such reactions. Therefore the absence of such signs could not be taken to exclude the presence of infection.

If an infectious agent is, in fact, present and responsible for the persisting deficiency of flow, we might be able to identify its presence by some favorable response to an agent capable of suppressing bacterial activity. The obvious experiment, then, is to give an antibiotic to a dog in hemorrhagic shock. In the first experiment, we gave the dog antibiotics intravenously. This reduced the mortality rate of five-hour shock from 85 per cent to 60 per cent—a suggestive, but not a definitive, result.

Having made certain that we were not introducing bacteria into the animal by our experimental manipulations, we considered next the possibility that the bacteria in the intestine might be the infecting agent. If so, they might be invading at too slow a rate to be detected by culture of the blood leading away from the intestine. Therefore, to assess the role of the intraintestinal bacteria, we attempted to reduce as far as possible the bacterial population of the intestine by giving antibiotics in the food for several days before inducing shock, and for good measure on the day of the experiment, several hours before starting the hemorrhage. This converted the mortality rate from 85 per cent to 12 per cent in the first twenty-five animals studied. With this observation we knew we had found something substantial.

After several hundred additional experiments with all sorts of antibiotics and all ways of giving them, we firmly established the fact that the effectiveness of the antibiotics depended not on the route by which they were administered, but on when they were given, and how susceptible the offending bacteria were to the antibiotic administered. The broad-range antibiotics worked if they were given in advance, but did not work to a significant extent if they were given during shock.

This evidence suggested to us the following general hypothesis: deficient flow, however produced, injures those tissues of the liver that are concerned with antibacterial defense; moreover, the longer the deficient flow lasts, the weaker does this defense become. Therefore, the longer the shock continues, the fewer the invading bacteria necessary to kill; they might indeed be too few to be detected by conventional culture techniques, for the latter may not be sensitive enough to allow growth when the inoculum is below 10^2 to 10^3 bacteria. If bacteria were not invading in significant numbers, the general thesis might still be valid, since endotoxins, which are bacterial poisons always present in the intestine, may be absorbed, and could escape destruction if the liver has lost its detoxicating power. Because of the failure of antibiotics to protect when they are given during shock, we assumed that the number of bacteria or the amount of bacterial toxin absorbed during the early phase of shock, i.e., prior to giving the antibiotic, must be enough to kill.

All these speculations were then tested in experimental animals. The first experiment explored the over-all antibacterial defense potential of the animal in shock, and compared it to that of the healthy animal in three ways: (a) the ability to destroy a dose of live bacteria injected intravenously; (b) the ability to detoxicate a given amount of bacterial poison of known killing power; and (c) the ability to deliver to an area of infection granulocytes, those white cells in the blood that leave the circulation in order to reach, engulf, and destroy bacteria. Every one of these functions was found to be severely impaired in the shocked animal.

Most impressive was the result of a quantitative test for the ability to detoxicate bacterial poison. This test showed that a rabbit, which was active and able to drink and eat several hours after recovery from shock of only two hours duration, had nevertheless been so damaged that it was killed by one one-hundred-thousandth to one one-millionth of the dose of toxin required to kill a normal rabbit. Thus it was made clear that only a brief exposure to shock so weakens the body defenses that less than one gamma (one millionth of a gram) of bacterial poison will be able to destroy the efficiency of the circulation and to kill an adult rabbit (average weight 5.5 pounds).

But in order to obtain positive proof of the general hypothesis we were required to demonstrate that toxin is present in the circulation, that it is of bacterial origin, and that it and not some other agent produces the injury to the blood vessels characteristic of the irretrievable state of shock. Accordingly, our next step was to search for the toxin.

A toxin had been sought for over thirty-five years, at least since the great physiologist, Walter Cannon, affirmed by inference the thesis that a toxin seemed to be involved in the disintegration of the body in shock that is caused by hemorrhage or massive trauma. But the search in almost all cases had been for an endogenous toxin, i.e., one that is exclusively derived from the products of disintegrating tissues. None had been identified. One reason for the failure lay in the methods employed to uncover the culprit. These methods used a normal animal as the test animal. Now, for our purpose, a normal animal has the crucial defect of possessing a substantial detoxicating potential; i.e., except for certain rare and exceptionally potent poisons, it is able to dispose of the quantity of such toxins as the body is likely to be exposed to in health and in a wide variety of disease states. Hence, if the test animal was to reveal the presence of a small quantity of toxin in a sample of blood from the shocked animal, the test animal must be one with its detoxicating potential weakened or destroyed.

We therefore employed as test animal a rabbit that had been transfused after being in shock for two hours. For this "two-hour animal," which recovers even though its defenses are down if it is not molested any further, dies, as stated above, if it is given a tiny dose of endotoxin. We reasoned that since a rabbit that had been in shock for five hours died, the detoxicating power of its liver was presumably so much weaker than that of a two-hour animal that its blood might contain free toxin. If this were true, we might be able to detect the presence of this toxin by putting the blood of the five-hour-shocked rabbit into a rabbit that had been in shock for only two hours, i.e., one that was extremely vulnerable to a very small dose of toxin.

Accordingly, the rabbit in shock for five hours was exsanguinated, and its blood was used to transfuse a rabbit in shock for only two hours. The latter rabbit, if transfused with its own shed blood, would have recovered promptly. But when blood from the five-hour-shocked donor was injected, it lay listless, its blood pressure failed to return to normal, and it died twelve to eighteen hours later. At autopsy it showed the injury to the intestine that is characteristic of death from prolonged shock. The donor's blood had converted a reversible state of shock into an irreversible state of shock. Further study revealed that the toxin was present not only in the blood, but also in the tissues of the donor animal.

The result was the same in dogs as in rabbits.

What is the nature of this toxin? If it is of bacterial origin, it should be possible to eliminate it from the blood of animals in prolonged shock by giving an antibiotic before the shock is induced. This theory proved to be correct. Not only was the blood of such animals in shock for five or six hours toxin-free, by the above test, but these animals survived. We then found that antibiotics that are given by mouth and that cannot be absorbed are also effective. This allowed us to conclude that the toxin was indeed of bacterial origin, and by the same token, we could also say that whether or not other toxins develop during shock, they were not involved in the phenomenon of irreversibility to transfusion. For if they were involved, the nonabsorbable antibiotic would not have prevented them from exerting their adverse effects and would not have prevented death.

The bacterial toxins normally present in the intestine are endotoxins. They are not secretory or excretory products of bacterial activity, but are the substance of the dead bacterial bodies. These endotoxins, from the chemical point of view, are poorly defined complexes of protein, lipide, and polysaccharide. Removal of the protein portion leaves the lipo-polysaccharide complex with undiminished toxicity. Therefore, if the toxin in the blood is a bacterial endotoxin, it should be possible to recover it from the blood by isolating that fraction that contains lipo-polysaccharides. Such fractions were prepared from normal blood, and proved to be entirely nontoxic. But similar fractions prepared from the blood of shocked animals killed test animals as readily as the whole blood from which they were isolated. Moreover, no other fraction of normal or shock blood was in any way toxic to the test animal. In short, the experiments showed the toxicity was entirely confined to the lipo-polysaccharide fraction, and to only that part of the fraction not present in normal plasma.

The next step was to see whether this fraction possessed the four biological properties characteristic of bacterial endotoxins. These properties are: (1) the ability, when injected into animals, to produce a characteristic fever curve; (2) the ability, when given in a sufficiently large dose, to produce shock and death; (3) the ability, after daily injection for some seven successive days, to induce such tolerance or resistance that the animal can then withstand one or more otherwise lethal doses of the toxin; and (4) the ability, when given to a properly prepared rabbit, to induce the so-called generalized Schwartzman reaction—a specific response characterized especially by a peculiar injury to the kidneys. The extracts of blood from shocked dogs and rabbits were found to possess every one of these four properties of bacterial endotoxins. The corresponding extracts from normal dogs and rabbits possessed none of them. Hence the toxin in the shocked blood was in fact an endotoxin.

Normally, bacteria or endotoxins entering the circulation are engulfed by scavenger cells massed in the liver, lung, and spleen. These cells are known collectively as the reticulo-endothelia system, or the R.E. system for short. This system is a most remarkable feature of the body's defense mechanisms. The cells of this system line the elaborate network of capillaries present everywhere throughout the liver, lung, and spleen. In the resting stage the cells look small and shrunken, but when stimulated they enlarge rapidly, take on amoeboid activity, engulf bacteria as well as other particulate material, and thus rapidly clear the bloodstream of unwanted foreign substances. To this extent they act like the circulating granulocytes; but R.E. cells differ from the latter in that they remain in large degree anchored to their original locus, whereas granulocytes traverse the capillary walls to reach a site of bacterial activity in tissues and there act as scavengers. R.E. cells are, in addition, capable of ingesting many more varieties of foreign material than are the granulocytes. But the most important function of the R.E. cells, for our investigation, is their special ability to take up and destroy endotoxin. By a little-understood process of adaptation they acquire, when exposed to rapidly repeated assault by bacteria or endotoxins, greater and greater facility to remove and destroy these endotoxins; thus they confer on the defense system of the normal animal an enormous increase in resistance.

This increase in resistance is expressed, in part, by the multiplication of the number of cells as well as an increase in their detoxicating activity in response to a noxious stimulus. Their response is so fast that the endotoxin is taken out of the blood in minutes instead of hours. In mice the liver doubles in size within twenty-four hours after an injection of a lipopolysaccharide. The R.E. cells in the liver, which are the most numerous and most active of the whole system, are strategically located so that bacteria or endotoxin entering the portal vein from the intestine must engage these cells in the sinusoids of the liver (Fig. 4). What escapes the liver will be seized by the same cells lining the capillaries in the lungs, and if not by the latter, then by those in the spleen, or, upon recirculation, by those in the liver. Thus it is that bacteria and other unwanted substances entering the circulation anywhere will eventually reach and be trapped in the R.E. system, with a speed depending on the time and degree of prior stimulation. Cells with a similar function, moreover, exist in great number throughout all the tissue spaces, where they seem to be derived from precursor cells or from membranes whose lining cells can convert to R.E. cells when necessary.

What seals the fate of the animal in shock is the failure of the R.E. cells to maintain their vital detoxicating ability. The functional failure of these cells, like that of other cells, results from the progressive decline in the rate of blood flow through the tissues in shock. Therefore, if infection develops with the R.E. system in a weakened state, the toxins from the bacteria are free to inflict irretrievable damage on the peripheral vessels, and so to convert reversible shock caused by some other agent into the irreversible type. According to our hypothesis, even if no infection is present, endotoxins normally entering the circulation from the intestine will continue to enter during shock; and if there is no defense against them, the irreversible state of shock will develop.

To check on the validity of this hypothesis it was important to examine the converse of this proposition, to wit: how would the animal react to an ordinarily fatal degree of shock if its R.E. system were prepared in advance by an increase in its ability to neutralize endotoxins? When we induced increased tolerance or resistance to bacterial endotoxins in a normal animal by daily injections of small doses of endotoxin for seven days, the animal withstood not only an otherwise lethal dose of toxin but also an otherwise lethal exposure to shock. After six hours of deep shock the rabbit did not take back any of the blood it had lost into the bottle, which indicated that there was no decompensation of circulation. When transfused thereafter, it began to recover promptly and was about its business a few hours later.

An increase in resistance can also occur spontaneously in consequence of accidental exposure to intestinal bacteria or their endotoxins. Unfortunately, this increase in resistance, whether spon-

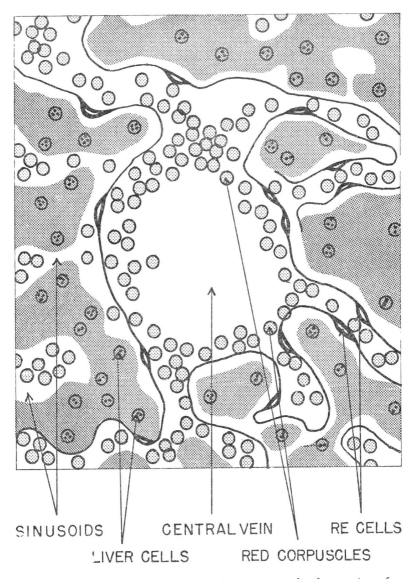

SINUSOIDS   CENTRAL VEIN   RE CELLS

LIVER CELLS   RED CORPUSCLES

FIG. 4. Schematic drawing from a photomicrograph of a portion of a liver lobule, showing the central vein, into which blood runs from the sinusoids and from which blood runs back to the heart. The coin-like bodies are the red corpuscles. The stippled areas are the liver cells containing circular bodies which are the nuclei of these cells. The lining of the sinusoids appears as a tortuous black border containing small bulbous

taneous or induced, is not retained for more than a few weeks thereafter—unlike the acquired resistance to smallpox, polio virus, tetanus,
or diphtheria, which persists for years.

Thus, animals as well as men differ widely in their resistance to
the same shock-inducing injury. Some have more resistance than
others by virtue not only of the time and extent of prior exposure
but also because of other factors; for example, the young are more
resistant than the old, the better nourished more resistant than the
poorly nourished, and so forth.

To test still more rigidly the main thesis that the collapse of the
R.E. system is the key injury in shock, we considered the following
proposition: if hemorrhagic shock is merely one agent that permits
bacterial endotoxins to injure the circulatory apparatus so as to
cause its irretrievable collapse and the victim's death, we should be
able to induce the state of irreversible shock and death by *any* agent
that eliminates the R.E. system's endotoxin-neutralizing power. Next
to shock, the most dramatic example of the rapid collapse of the R.E.
system is that which follows exposure to a lethal dose of whole-body
radiation. Not only are most of the R.E. cells destroyed, but the
adaptive responses of the rest are limited. The result is that about
five days after the exposure the bacteria from the respiratory or
intestinal tracts invade and multiply unhindered, and produce septic
shock and death within hours.

A quicker and easier way to disable the R.E. system is to saturate
the R.E. system with thorium dioxide, which is a foreign particulate
material that is avidly consumed by the R.E. cells. This substance,
like India ink, acts to blockade the R.E. system. For several hours
after the injection of such materials, the R.E. cells are less able to
take up other substances, including endotoxins, so that if we administer a very small dose of endotoxin during those hours (but not
later, e.g., twelve to twenty-four hours), it produces fatal shock.

We repeated this well-known experiment, but, instead of giving
the thorium dioxide-treated animal a dose of endotoxins, we produced
hemorrhagic shock for only five minutes. This also resulted in irre-

---

enlargements at intervals. The latter are the lining cells known as reticulo-
endothelial or Kupffer cells; here they appear as small inactive structures.
When stimulated they swell up, multiply, and engulf particulate and non-
particulate macromolecular substances, both foreign and native to the
body. These cells, when very active, may be so numerous and prominent
as to choke the sinusoidal channels.

versible shock and death. Then, instead of giving endotoxin or inducing shock for five minutes, we gave a small additional dose of thorium dioxide. Again, the animal went into shock and died. When examined at death, all these animals gave evidence of death from endotoxin, even though in two of the three described types of experiment no endotoxin was administered. Thus, we could assume that endotoxin was continually getting into the circulation. In the third experiment, in which a first dose of thorium dioxide was followed by a tiny second dose two or three hours later, it was the second tiny dose that was the *coup de grâce*. It was like hitting a man after he was down; the second dose destroyed what remained of the defense potential already weakened by the first dose, so that endotoxin coming in from somewhere could do its work on the circulation without hindrance. From where did this endotoxin come? There is no known reservoir except that in the intestine, and perhaps also in the mouth, nose, and throat.

Thus the intestinal bacteria stand as a constant threat to the organism. They threaten it not only in hemorrhage or in massive trauma, but also in less overt circumstances. Illnesses like cancer, severe diabetes, ulcerative colitis, and so forth deplete the integrity of tissues in general and of the R.E. system in particular, and endotoxins are less and less effectively neutralized. A time arrives when the endotoxins no longer can be resisted. The actual cause of death in such diseases, then, may be a terminal state of irreversible shock due either to overt infection or intestinal bacteria rather than the disease itself.

The shock problem is a challenge to develop methods that bolster the antibacterial defense of the body. We strengthen our own bacterial defense every day of our lives to a small degree when we brush our teeth or chew hard food, and thus force bacteria into the bloodstream. But we must seek more potent and definitive ways to achieve increased resistance and to achieve it rapidly, so that the resistance of individuals like the poor pawnbroker will be made equal to that of the eighteen-year-old soldier. Another challenging objective is to find an antidote to endotoxins.

This account began with a statement concerning the nature of the problems of shock caused by hemorrhage, and pointed out that our task was to find out why the victim of hemorrhagic shock sometimes fails to respond to transfusion. Through our exploration of the mechanism of irreversible collapse caused by hemorrhage, we have uncovered fundamental features of the pathology of other types of shock as well—those caused by various forms of massive injury, and severe infection. Hence we have come to understand more fully one of the most common causes of death.

BIBLIOGRAPHY

1. Davis, H. A. *Shock and Allied Forms of Failure of the Circulation.* New York: Grune and Stratton, 1949.
2. Wiggers, C. J. *Physiology of Shock.* New York: Commonwealth Fund, 1950.
3. *Symposium on Shock.* Research and Development Division, Office of the Surgeon General, U. S. Army (Monograph), May 1951.
4. Fine, Jacob. *Bacterial Factor in Traumatic Shock.* Springfield, Ohio: C. C. Thomas, 1954.
5. *Physiopathology of the Reticulo-Endothelial System.* Edited by B. Benacerraf and J. F. Delafresnaye, Oxford: Blackwell Scientific Publications, January 1957.

NOTES ON CONTRIBUTORS

RAYMOND ARON was born in 1905 in Paris, France. He is Professor of Sociology at the Sorbonne and, through his editorials in *Le Figaro,* one of Europe's best-known commentators on world affairs. The methodological critique of historiography has long been among his main concerns, exemplified in such early works as *La Sociologie Allemande Contemporaine* and *Introduction à la Philosophie de l'Histoire.* His books published in the United States are *The Century of Total War, The Opium of the Intellectuals,* and *France Defeats EDC* (with Daniel Lerner).

MARTIN DEUTSCH was born in Vienna, Austria, in 1917. At Massachusetts Institute of Technology since 1937, he has been Professor of Physics since 1953. His major fields of research and teaching have been the study of radiation, the study of fission processes, and nuclear spectroscopy. He has published widely in technical journals, and has co-authored *The Science and Engineering of Nuclear Power* (with Clark Goodman).

ERIK H. ERIKSON, born in Frankfurt, Germany, in 1902, received his training and began his clinical career at the Vienna Psychoanalytic Institute. He has been a practicing psychoanalyst since 1933, and a training psychoanalyst in institutes of the American Psychoanalytic Association since 1942. Now on the staff of the Austen Riggs Center in Stockbridge, Massachusetts, he also holds a professorship in psychiatry at the University of Pittsburgh School of Medicine, and this year, is a Visiting Professor of International Communication at Massachusetts Institute of Technology. In addition to papers and monographs on clinical subjects, he has written *Childhood and Society,* and *Young Man Luther: A Study in Psychoanalysis and History.*

JACOB FINE was born in Brockton, Massachusetts, in 1900, received the M.D. at Harvard in 1924, and completed graduate training in surgery at Massachusetts General Hospital in 1927. He has been Surgeon-in-Chief at Beth Israel Hospital, Brookline, Massachusetts, since 1948. He joined the faculty of the surgical department of Harvard Medical School in 1932, and has been Professor of Surgery since 1949. In addition to his contributions to medical journals, he has written *Care of Surgical Patients.*

HENRY M. HART, JR. was born in 1904 in Butte, Montana. He was secretary to Justice Louis D. Brandeis of the United States Supreme Court from 1931 to 1932, has been on the Harvard Law School faculty since 1932, and is now Charles Stebbins Fairchild Professor of Law. From 1937 to 1946, he served as attorney or counsel for a number of federal agencies and offices. Some of his special areas of teaching, research, and publication are the legal process, criminal law, and federal courts and federal systems. He has co-authored *Federal Courts and the Federal System* (with Herbert Wechsler).

PAUL F. LAZARSFELD was born in Vienna, Austria, in 1901. He has been Professor of Sociology at Columbia University since 1940, Associate Director of the Bureau of Applied Social Research, and consultant on mass media communications. Among his book publications are *Research Memorandum on the Family in the Depression* (with Samuel A. Stouffer), *Radio and the Printed Page, Radio Research* (with F. Stanton), *The People's Choice, The People Look at Radio* (with Harry Field), and *The Academic Mind* (with Wagner Thielens, Jr.), currently in production.

DANIEL LERNER, born in New York City in 1917, is Professor of Sociology and International Communication at Massachusetts Institute of Technology, and a Senior Research Associate of its Center for International Studies. During World War II, he served as Chief Editor of the intelligence branch of the Psychological Warfare Division, SHAEF, and as Chief of Intelligence in the Information Control Division of the Office of Military Government, U.S.A. His books include *Sykewar, Propaganda in War and Crisis, The Nazi Elite, The Policy Sciences* (with H. D. Lasswell), and *The Passing of Traditional Society.*

JOHN T. MCNAUGHTON was born in 1921 in Bicknell, Indiana. He has been at the Harvard Law School since 1953, and Professor of Law since 1956. He was on the economic and legal staff of the Economic Cooperation Administration in Paris from 1949 to 1951, and Editor of the *Pekin* (Illinois) *Daily Times* from 1951 to 1953. His principal field is Evidence. His publications include *State v. Hauptmann, The Last Will and Testament of Mabel Seymour Greer, Workbook in Judicial Proof,* and *Handbook of Massachusetts Evidence* (with W. Barton Leach).

Guide to Further Readings

This list of readings gives neither a general bibliography nor specific sources for the papers in this Colloquium. It is intended, rather, as a highly selective guide through the extensive literature on concept and method—with specific attention to Evidence and Inference—in each of the fields covered in these chapters. Further references will be found in the titles here listed. While the authors have been most cooperative in selecting titles, responsibility for this list rests with the editor.

INTRODUCTION:

ON EVIDENCE AND INFERENCE

The great general histories of science (those by Charles H. Haskins, George Sarton, Charles Singer, Lynn Thorndike) do not focus on the interaction of concept and method. The most useful single-volume, readily-available history is:

Dampier, Sir William C. *A History of Science and Its Relations with Philosophy and Religion,* New York: Macmillan, 1946.

For a clear introduction showing the passage from classical to modern mathematical analysis of logical relations in evidence and inference, see:

Clifford, William K. *The Common Sense of the Exact Sciences,* New York: Knopf, 1946.
Cohen, Morris R., and Nagel, Ernest. *An Introduction to Logic and Scientific Method,* New York: Harcourt, Brace, 1934.

The modern theory of inference is elaborated, with special reference to empirical procedures in the natural sciences, in:

Churchman, C. Wayne. *Theory of Experimental Inference,* New York: Macmillan, 1948.
Wisdom, John O. *Foundations of Inference in Natural Science,* London: Methuen, 1952.

Application of formal modern theory to evidence and inference in the social sciences is still an underdeveloped area of intellectual effort. The initiatives of Guttman, Lazarsfeld and others may be reviewed in:

STOUFFER, SAMUEL A. (ed.). *Measurement and Prediction*, Princeton, New Jersey: Princeton University Press, 1951.

The evolution of concepts and methods for "the proper study of mankind," the axiomatics underlying the logic of research on human behavior, is presented in:

SHERRINGTON, SIR CHARLES. *Man On His Nature*, New York: Anchor Books, 1955.

LERNER, DANIEL (ed.). *The Human Meaning of the Social Sciences*, New York: Meridian Books, 1959.

IN HISTORY

The dozen titles below were selected largely to introduce some major views of historiography in modern European thinking, using only the literature readily available in English.

COLLINGWOOD, R. G. *The Idea of History*, New York: Oxford University Press, 1956.

COMMITTEE ON HISTORIOGRAPHY, *Theory and Practice of Historical Study: A Report of the Committee on Historiography*, New York: Social Science Research Council, 1946.

CROCE, BENEDETTO. *History, Its Theory and Practice*, New York: Harcourt, Brace, 1923.

DREY, WILLIAM. *Laws and Explanation in History*, London: Oxford University Press, 1957.

GARDINER, PATRICK. *The Nature of Historical Explanation*, London: Oxford University Press, 1957.

HOOK, SIDNEY. *From Hegel to Marx*, New York: Humanities Press, 1950.

LANGER, WILLIAM L. "The Next Assignment," *American Historical Review*, LXIII (January 1958), 283-304.

MEYERHOFF, HANS. *Philosophy of History in Our Time*, New York: Doubleday, 1959.

POPPER, KARL R. *The Poverty of Historicism*, Boston: Beacon Press, 1957.

SALVEMINI, GAETANO. *Historian and Scientist*, Cambridge, Mass.: Harvard University Press, 1939.

SHILS, EDWARD A., AND FINCH, HENRY A. (eds.). *Max Weber on the Methodology of the Social Sciences*, Glencoe: Free Press, 1949.

WHITE, MORTON. *Social Thought in America*, Boston: Beacon Press, 1957.

IN LAW

For the best available account in concise and readable form of the the rules of evidence:

MAGUIRE, J. M. *Evidence—Common Sense and Common Law*, Chicago: The Foundation Press, 1947, pp. 45-50.

For one of the classical expositions of the theory of judicial proof:

WIGMORE, J. H. *The Science of Judicial Proof*, Boston: Little, Brown & Co., 3rd ed., 1937.

For a discussion of probability in the terms which apply in judicial fact-finding tribunals:

KEYNES, J. M. *A Treatise on Probability*, London: Macmillan & Co., 1921, pp. 20-40.

For a perceptive analysis of the troublesome problems of the relation between law and fact as they present themselves in the context of adjudication by an administrative agency:

JAFFE, L. L. "Judicial Review: Question of Law," *Harvard Law Review* LXIX (1955), 239; "Judicial Review: Question of Fact," *Ibid.*, LXIX (1956), 1020.

For as nearly satisfactory an account as there is in print of the difficulties involved in putting a court in possession of the data which are relevant in the formulation of just grounds of decision:

"Note, Social and Economic Facts—Appraisal of Suggested Techniques for Presenting Them to the Courts," *Harvard Law Review*, LXI 1948), 692.

For an examination of the resources of an administrative agency, in comparison with those of a court, for informing itself about matters of general or legislative fact:

DAVIS, K. C. *Administrative Law*, St. Paul: West Publishing Co., 1951, Chapter 12.

For an antidote to the views which the authors have expressed, and for what to them seems a wholly unrealistic conception of the potential role of experts in resolving questions about what kinds of statutes ought, and what kinds ought not, to be enacted:

COHEN, J. "Towards Realism in Legisprudence," *Yale Law Journal*, LIX (1950), 886.

IN CLINICS (PSYCHIATRIC)

BENJAMIN, J. D. "Methodological Considerations in the Validation and Elaboration of Psychoanalytical Personality Theory," *Amer. J. Orthopsychiat.,* XX (1950), 139-156.

BRENMAN, M. "Research in Psychotherapy. Round Table, 1947," *Am. J. Orthopsychiat.,* XVIII (1948), 92-118.

———. "Problems in Clinical Research. Round Table, 1946," *Amer. J. Orthopsychiat.,* XIX (1947), 196-230.

ESCALONA, S. "Problems in Psychoanalytic Research," *Int. J. Psa.,* XXXIII (1952), 11-21.

KRIS, E. "The Nature of Psychoanalytic Propositions and Their Validation." In: *Freedom and Experience.* Essays presented to Horace M. Kallen, New York: Cornell Univ. Press, 1947, pp. 239-259.

LOMBARD, G. F. F. "Self-Awareness and Scientific Method," *Science,* CXII (1950), 289-293.

MEEHL, PAUL. *Clinical Versus Statistical Prediction: A Theoretical Analysis and a Review of the Evidence.* Minneapolis: University of Minnesota Press, 1954.

PUMPIAN-MINDLIN, E. (ed.). *Psychoanalysis as Science,* Stanford: Stanford University Press, 1952. Five distinguished papers on experimental approaches to psychodynamics and psychotherapy (E. R. Hilgard); problems and techniques of psychoanalytic validation (L. S. Kubie); and the relation of psychoanalysis to biological and social sciences (E. Pumpian-Mindlin).

THORNE, FREDERICK C. "The Clinical Method in Science," *Amer. Psychologist,* II (1947), 166.

IN SURVEYS (ATTITUDE RESEARCH)

The general theory of index-formation is exemplified in:

LAZARSFELD, P. F., AND ROSENBERG, M. (eds.). *Language of Social Research,* Glencoe: Free Press, 1955, Section I.

An inventory of group properties as used in current sociological literature is provided by:

MERTON, R. K. *Social Theory and Social Structure,* 2d ed., Glencoe: Free Press, 1957, pp. 311-325.

A good discussion of the general principles involved is given by:

BLAU, P. M. *American Journal of Sociology,* LXIII (1957), p. 58 ff.

Many concrete examples of the treatment of multivariant statistical relations will be found in:

HYMAN, H. H. *Survey Design and Analysis,* Glencoe: Free Press, 1955.

The organizing use of mathematics is shown at its best in:

SIMON, H. A. *Models of Man,* New York: Wiley, 1957.

The literature on group problem-solving models is reviewed by:

LORGE, I. D., AND SOLOMON, H. *Psychometrica,* XX (1955), p. 139 ff.

IN LABORATORIES (NUCLEAR PHYSICS)

BORN, MAX. *Experiment and Theory in Physics,* New York: Dover, 1955.
BRAITHWAITE, RICHARD B. *Scientific Explanation,* Cambridge: Cambridge University Press, 1953.
POPPER, KARL. *Logik der Forschung* (see forthcoming English translation).
BOHR, NIELS. "Discussion with Einstein on Epistemological Problems in Atomic Physics," in *Albert Einstein: Philosopher-Scientist,* Paul Arthur Schilpp (ed.), Evanston: Northwestern University Press, 1949.

IN MEDICINE

The following eleven references illustrate the process of trial, error, retrial in medical research through reports on classic cases, old and new, of empirical experimentation.

On the discovery that the cause of diabetes is a deficiency of the pancreas:

VON MERING, J., AND MINKOWSKI, O. "Diabetes Mellitus After Extirpation of the Pancreas," *Arch. f. exper. Path. U. Pharmacol.,* 1889-90, 26, 375.

On the discovery of insulin:

BANTING, F. G., AND BEST, C. H. "The Internal Secretion of the Pancreas," *J. Lab. & Clin. Med.,* 1922, 72, 65.

On the transmission of malarial parasites to man by mosquitoes:

ROSS, SURGEON MAJOR RONALD. "Pigmented Cells in Mosquitoes," *British Med. J.,* 1898, 1, 550.
REED, WALTER, CARROLL, JAMES, AGREMONTE, A., AND LAZEAR, JESSE W. "Etiology of Yellow Fever," *Med. Rec.,* 1900, 6, 790, 791-793, 796.

FIESER, LOUIS F. "The Synthesis of Vitamin K_1," *Science,* Jan. 12, 1940, Vol. 91, 2350, 31-36.

HARVEY, WILLIAM. "On the Motion of the Heart and Blood," trans. by Robert Willis, Syndenhem Society, 1847.

KOCH, ROBERT. "The Etiology of Tuberculosis," Berliner Klinische Wochenschrift, 1882, 19, 221; trans. by Dr. & Mrs. Max Pinner, *Am. Rev. Tuber.,* March 1932.

BEAUMONT, WILLIAM. *Experiments and Observations on the Gastric Juice,* Cambridge (Mass.): Harvard University Press, 1929.

BERNARD, CLAUDE. *Introduction to the Study of Experimental Medicine,* trans. by Henry Copley Greene, New York: Macmillan, 1927.

CANNON, WALTER B. *Bodily Changes in Pain, Hunger, Fear and Rage,* 2nd edition, New York: D. Appleton & Co., 1929.

LOEWI, OTTO. *On the Humoral Transmission of the Heart Nerve Impulse,* Pfluger's Archive, 1921, 189, 239.